TOM the ANGEL CAT

Kai Herndon

Wasteland Press

www.wastelandpress.net
Shelbyville, KY USA

Tom the Angel Cat
by Kai Herndon

First Printing – August 2014
ISBN: 978-1-60047-981-6

Printed in the U.S.A.

0   1   2   3   4   5

Dedication

I would like to dedicate this book to all the wonderful people at the Salem VA Medical Center Palliative Care Unit, who treated my dad with much love, respect and honor in his last hours. And especially to Tom, who is a real live cat, of whom I took a few liberties concerning his life story. He continues to be a vital part of the Palliative Care Unit today.

I would also like to thank the illustrator of my book, Connor Jones, a very talented fourth-grader at Mountain View Elementary School in Roanoke Va., who does wonderful work for homeless animals at the Angels of Assisi, by donating the proceeds of his art work. Many thanks to Betsy Day of Brighter Day Editing, without her help I would have been lost.

To my family, I give many thanks, without their support, this tribute to my dad would have been a tremendous task alone.

My final dedication goes to Tom the Angel Cat, one of Gods' less fortunate creatures, a stray alley cat, who gave comfort and guidance to my dad's spiritual journey home and without his conscious understanding renewed my faith in the Lord, by merely looking up!.

TABLE OF CONTENTS

CHAPTER ONE:

A New Home

Ah, the pure joy of it, so cozy and warm I am. "Look how cute he is," said the little old lady with the sad brown eyes.

"Just a bundle of orange fluff," replied Miss Sally. "And to think this little kitten was sleeping with a dog; quite unusual indeed," commented the old lady.

I looked at Sheba, the Samoyed she was referring to, and yawned as I lay curled up in her fluffy white tail. "Hey, kitten, here's another one looking to give you a good, friendly home," Sheba said.

"But Sheba, *this* is home, the only home I remember. I have no memory of my mom or my brother or my sister, just you and Miss Sally," said the kitten.

"Baby kitten, you are the only one of your family that the cat-snatchers didn't find, and that's because Miss Sally found you first and brought you home so you wouldn't starve to death. She fed you with a human's baby-bottle, and I kept you warm," answered Sheba.

"Tell me all about it Sheba, please," the kitten begged.

"Well, little one, your story began when Miss Sally and I took our usual morning stroll; this being a fairly bad neighborhood, Miss Sally always took me along for safety," Sheba recalled. "Miss Sally has always had a fondness for the less fortunate, whether it be human or animal," she continued. "As we came closer to Old Mr. Baker's house, which was sorely in need of repair, Miss Sally stopped to check in on him, because he wasn't in the best of health, you see, and couldn't do a lot of things for himself. Poor Old Mr. Baker couldn't afford to heat his house, so he was wrapped up in several blankets and wore all of the few clothes he owned, to keep warm," she said, and she shivered at the memory. "And he never had enough to eat, so Miss Sally always brought him a brown bag full of leftovers, which he shared with your momma, so that she could make milk for her three baby kittens, one of which was you, little one," she said, licking the kitten's head. "Old Mr. Baker informed us that the City had condemned his house. He had to go to live in a homeless shelter, and he said that the people would be there at any time to take him there. They wouldn't let him take your momma or you and your siblings with him. He also said that the cat-snatchers were somewhere in the area, and had been told to come to his house to take all of you to the pound. He begged Miss Sally to take you all to safety." Sheba recalled the intense moment. "You and your family were in Old Mr. Baker's bedroom closet, just starting to nurse, eyes still closed because you guys were only a few days old," she said.

"Was my mother beautiful?" asked the kitten.

"Yes, she was, solid white, just like me. Your siblings were black-and-white; you were the only one that looked like your father, according to your mother," Sheba answered.

"Now let me finish the story.

As I was saying, a knock came at the door and the City people were there to get Old Mr. Baker out of the house, and right behind them, coming in the door like gangbusters, were the cat-snatchers. Miss Sally only had time to grab one of you and hide you under her coat, and they scooped up your family and took them off to the pound. Poor Old Mr. Baker, blankets trailing behind him, was escorted by several mean-looking gentlemen to a large black car and whisked away, and that's how you came to be part of our family," she said tenderly to the weepy-eyed kitten.

Sheba stood up and shook her luxurious fur coat and curled her tail over her back. "Today, little kitten, you will find a new family," she proclaimed.

The little old lady and Miss Sally were still talking in the far corner of the kitchen. "Here they come, so sit up straight, stop scratching yourself, and look alert," barked Sheba.

"Miss Sally, I think I'm going to take him home with me today; he's just the right companion for me in my small house, and I am alone now that my dear husband has passed away, but with a cat in the house, I won't be so lonely anymore," the little old lady said.

"I think I'll simply call him Tom—that's a good name for an orange alley cat," she stated.

Miss Sally picked me up and handed me to the little old lady.

"Tom, meet Miss Opal," she said. Miss Opal gently took me from Miss Sally's arms and cradled me close to her chest.

"Yes sir, Tom, you are going to have a fine new home, lots to eat, fun things to play with, and neat places to explore," she said.

I looked down at Sheba, my best friend, and I felt sad to be leaving her, but just for a minute, because when I looked into Miss Opal's eyes as she was stroking my head, I saw even more sadness there, and I thought to myself, maybe this is where I belong, after all.

"Life with Miss Opal is pure heaven—the best food, served in shiny silvery bowls, milk anytime I want it, toys everywhere, and the run of the house; life is good," thought Tom. As the years rolled on by, I grew into a very handsome orange alley cat, if I say so myself. King of the castle, except of course for Dinkles, the one and only mouse in the house—the only mouse that I knew, and could never seem to catch.

"Stop running so fast, Dinkles, I don't care if you eat that cheese or not. Miss Opal left it there on the table on purpose, anyway," said Tom.

Dinkles and I had a strange kind of relationship; he'd run from me and then stop just short of his hole in the wall, sit down on his small gray rump, and begin to talk.

Dinkles knew everything that went on in our house. "Tom, I'll bet you didn't know that Miss Opal is going away, far away, to a place called a 'nursing home,' did you?" asked Dinkles. "I heard Mr. Plunkett say so yesterday, and Mr. Plunkett, being her nurse and all, he would surely know," he said. Dinkles and I didn't like Mr. Plunkett very much. Whenever he came to check on Miss Opal, we would try and play a trick on him. Because the nurse was deathly afraid of mice, Dinkles would sometimes hide under Miss Opal's covers.

The minute Mr. Plunkett pulled them back, Dinkles would stand on his hind legs and make menacing squeaking noises at him. The nurse would run, screaming like a little girl. Miss Opal didn't mind, because she didn't care much for Mr. Plunkett, either.

"Snap out of your daydream, Tom; didn't you hear the disturbing news?" asked Dinkles.

"I know that Miss Opal has been feeling out of sorts lately, and the nurse is here almost every day," replied Tom. "What's to become of us, then?" he asked the mouse.

"I don't know about you, Tom, but I have lots of family in the neighborhood I can live with, but I guess you're on your own," said Dinkles. "Just make sure you always hide from the cat-snatchers; they take you to a terrible place, I hear," he whispered.

"I don't want anything to happen to Miss Opal. I know that she isn't feeling well, but to go away and leave me...! I must find out for myself if what Dinkles says is true," thought Tom.

Into Miss Opal's bedroom Tom crept. Jumping onto the bed, he landed squarely on Miss Opal's chest. She opened her eyes slightly when she felt the strong thump and heard the familiar purring, and rubbed Tom lovingly behind his ears. "My dear friend, you have been such a blessing to me all these years," she said. "My beautiful Tom, I have to go away, to a place you cannot go. God is calling me home to heaven, and it will not be long now, but I want you to know that I will be with you always, Tom; just look up," she said softly.

"Heaven? What's heaven?" thought Tom. "Is that the same as cat heaven? Don't people have nine lives, too?" he asked himself under his breath.

I slept with Miss Opal the whole night, and the next morning Mr. Plunkett arrived with lots of strange people all dressed in long white coats. They carried Miss Opal to a red, shiny ambulance. She never opened her eyes or spoke another word to me. I was scared, and very sad, to see my best friend leave. "She is close to her heaven now," said Dinkles, as he sat beside me and watched her leave.

"Dinkles, I don't know if I like this place called heaven. It takes the people that you love away and leaves you on your own," Tom said, his voice full of emotion.

At that very moment, Tom heard a soft whisper in his mind. "Not so, Tom, heaven is a wondrous place, and God has a place for you, Tom, and for all of your nine lives."

Contemplating this, Tom did not have enough time to react when Mr. Plunkett came back into the house, scooped him up, and unceremoniously dumped him on the front stoop, locking the front door behind him.

"I've never been so glad to get rid of a patient before. I'll never have to come back to this god-awful house full of rodents and an ugly alley cat that doesn't know its place," said Mr. Plunkett. "As for you, Tom, you're on your own. Even though Miss Opal asked me to watch over you, that's one promise I am *not* going to keep," he said, glaring at Tom with disgust.

I sat there and watched Miss Opal, my only family and best friend, being driven away in the red shiny truck.

CHAPTER TWO:

The Cat-Snatchers

"Boy, am I cold, wet, and really, really hungry, all at the same time," thought Tom, as he lay hidden under the stoop of the old abandoned house that once had been his home. Staying out of the chilly spring rain and away from the cat-snatchers was his main goal every day. "Good grief, here comes Steel Blu—I wonder what he wants?" he asked himself.

Steel Blu, a sleek, black, green-eyed house cat, stopped in front of Tom to shoot the breeze and clean his last meal of gourmet chicken cat food from his long, black whiskers. "Nasty day today! Say, Tom, have you had your dinner yet?" he asked. "If not, I just passed an overturned garbage can two blocks back, in front of DooDaw's Chicken Shack; you'd probably find some good scraps in there. Of course, I can't attest to the taste of the cuisine, since I am, after all, a bona fide house cat, and eat only the very best canned food," he said in his usual haughty tone.

Tom, the abandoned alley cat, sat up and tried to make his scrawny body and mud-spattered orange coat seem regal. "Have to show some pride, you know," he thought to himself. "Well, sir, I have just eaten one of the biggest and juiciest field mice you've ever seen," said Tom. "He ran by here, and all I had to do was put out my paw; it was no trouble at all," he added matter-of-factly.

"Well, that *is* great news; eating mice keeps your coat sleek, and I guess you have to keep up your appearance in case you ever have a chance for a real home again; nobody wants a skinny, dull-coated pet," snickered Steel Blu, as he licked his rotund belly. "See you later, cat—I'm going home to my family; I just *can't* take much of this outdoor living," he remarked, walking away with his tail straight up in the air.

"Good riddance! I can't stand those uppity, lazy, good-for-nothing house cats," thought Tom. He curled himself up into a ball and lay down on the shredded rug to keep warm, crossing his paws the way Miss Opal had taught him, and saying his prayers before he went to sleep. He prayed the same prayer every night: "Lord, I don't know why you made me an ugly ol' orange alley cat that nobody wants; I guess you had your reasons, but if you ever have a mind to, I'd surely like to have a family and a home someday, and a purpose, Lord, I really like purposes, amen," prayed Tom.

"Tom, Tom, wake up!" said Bailey and Chewy, Tom's two miscreant cat-acquaintances. Bailey, who always looked scared because of his crossed eyes, was nervously picking at his grey-and-white fur. Chewy, whom all the animals in the neighborhood said looked like a mad scientist because of the black mustache under his nose and all his missing fur, wildly chased his tail in a circle, talking the whole time.

"The cat-snatchers are in the neighborhood, just down the street, they surely are," said Chewy.

"Yeah, they're catching everybody," said Bailey.

"We're heading to the west dump—want to come along? It's safer there," said Chewy.

"I'll take my chances here; anyway, they don't want an ol' scrawny orange tabby like me," said Tom. "They won't look for me under this stoop, and besides, I'm too tired to run away."

"Suit yourself, but we're gone; take care of yourself," the two worn-looking cats said in unison. Off down the road the pair scampered, climbing up the big pine tree, then over the tall palisade fence and out of sight.

Life had been really difficult since Miss Opal went away. Tom missed his nice, warm bed and his friend, Dinkles. Now and then, Dinkles came by to visit with him and brought him a piece of cheese. They reminisced about all the jokes they had played on Mr. Plunkett, and played their chasing game, just for old times' sake. Tom wondered about Miss Sally and Sheba; he hoped they were doing well, and he wished he could remember how to get back to them, but it had been a long time since they'd all left Miss Sally's home, and his memory wasn't as sharp as it had been when he was a kitten. Miss Opal had taken him home in a car, so he couldn't recognize any landmarks if he tried. "I guess I'm all on my own forever," he thought to himself.

Tom drifted back to sleep, only to be awakened by shouts of excitement.

"Here's one, just as mangy as they come, he looks to be a real menace, this one does," said the tall, thin man in the green raincoat, as he squatted down looking at Tom, waving a large net on a pole to and fro. Before Tom could rub the cat-sleep from his eyes, he found himself upside-down in the net.

"Got him," said the tall, thin man to his partner, an obese gentleman named Ollie. "What do you think?

Ollie, huffing and puffing, was trying to catch up. He stopped and eyeballed Tom. "Well, Bart, he's quite a sorry specimen of a cat, but I just can't tell; he might clean up nicely, and we could fatten him up a bit, and *someone* might want him," he replied.

"Well, if they don't, I guess he'll go to you-know-where—cat heaven," chuckled Bart.

"Oh, dear me, this is *not* what I've been praying for," thought Tom.

Tom was thrust into a rusted metal cage and shoved into the back of the blue cat-snatcher truck. The air inside the truck had a familiar smell to it, a sweet-but-bad smell, similar to the odor he'd caught a whiff of just before Miss Opal had left him. The death-smell, Dinkles had informed him, was the one sure sign that a loved one was going home to heaven.

CHAPTER THREE:

Death Row

We arrived at an old, crumbling brown building set by itself on a weedy lot next to a loud and swift-running creek. "Tinker Creek is running a bit high today; we might need to keep an eye on it for a while," Bart said in a conversational tone.

"You'd better believe I will—it might flood this place again," replied Ollie.

I was taken into the brown building in my metal cage and not so gently dumped on the floor, in front of the largest, meanest-looking woman I'd ever seen. "So, this is the new one. He sure smells bad, and I'd bet he's wormy and flea-bitten to boot," remarked Hazel in her harsh, loud, booming voice. "Good candidate for you-know-what," she laughed. Ollie and Bart looked at me and then at each other and nodded their heads in agreement.

"Where did you find him?" she asked. "Under a porch stoop at an abandoned house in Old Southeast. I think that the old lady that used to live there died years ago," Bart answered. "He probably used to live there with her. We've been trying to catch him for a long time," Ollie chimed in.

In gleeful tones, Hazel said, "Put him in the ten-day cell. I don't imagine anyone will really want to adopt him, and we know that nobody's looking for him, so ten days are enough.

"Ten days, just ten days, ten days to what?" Tom asked himself.

Ollie, still out of breath because of his girth, lifted him up and carried him, cage and all, into a dingy yellow room with peeling paint and large cracks in the walls.

"A cold and barren, depressing place indeed. Compared to these accommodations, the front stoop at Miss Opal's seemed like a mansion," thought Tom, as he adjusted his eyesight to the dimly lit room. He noticed that the only decoration on the wall was a sign that read "TEN DAYS/NO EXCEPTIONS."

"Sorry, fellow, that your new abode is a bit lacking in creature comforts, but at least you'll be fed and kept out of the rain," said Ollie, peering in at Tom.

If he hadn't known better, he'd have thought he'd been here forever. People came in at all hours to see the other animals and children yelled excitedly about their new-found pets, never once looking in at him. The days and nights were very lonely. Tom wondered if this was the kind pf place his mother and siblings had been taken to, all those years ago; he hoped it was a better place than this. Tom prayed for a miracle—that Miss Sally and his good friend

Sheba would come bouncing through the door to rescue him as they had so long ago.

"No such luck, I guess, because the only one coming through that door is Hazel, with her clipboard. She probably has a vision of me upside-down with my legs in the air, all stiff, mean old Bart right behind her, ready to poke at me to make sure I haven't gained any weight, I suppose," thought Tom.

"Nine, eight, seven, six, five days left," said Bart to Hazel.

"Nobody has even looked at this mangy orange tabby, and here Ollie wants to clean him up and feed him a little more to fatten him up," he said as he cleaned out Tom's cage.

"Not on my watch he won't, it would just be a waste of good supplies; besides, he won't be around much longer, anyway" replied Hazel.

Bart and Hazel left the room, leaving the half-hinged door slightly ajar. All day and all night the howls and meows of the lucky ones in the adoption rooms filled the air.

Tom settled down after supper to say his prayers, crossing his paws as Miss Opal had taught him. "Cat prayers," she used to say, "for God's special orange cats."

"Lord, I'm not sure what you had in mind for me; being just a cat and all, I can't really do much but chase and eat mice—other mice, not Dinkles' family of course; or lay in the sun and purr a lot, but I hope Miss Opal was right and that you *do* have a special plan in mind for an ol' alley cat, and soon, too!"

"Move your paws off of the bowl, cat, you're tipping me over," shouted Randall, the resident cockroach.

Stopped short in his prayers, Tom glared at Randall, who was perched on the side of his feeding bowl. Randall was the only other living thing that Tom had spoken to in this terrible place since he had been brought here ten days before. Randall came each evening after suppertime to clean up any scraps that Tom might have left. "Who are you talking to, Tom?" asked Randall, his antennae twitching this way and that.

"I'm saying my prayers; don't you do that, Randall?" asked Tom.

"Sure I do; we roaches have an edited version: we've got such a short life-span, you know, we've got to plan ahead quickly," giggled Randall.

"I need to get out of here." Tom felt desperate.

"What would you do if you *could* get out of here, Tom, my boy?" asked Randall, in between bites of Tom's leftover crumbs.

"I'm not sure, but I think that God wants me to help all living things that are running out of time—you know, before they go to heaven—to comfort them, just to be there. But it doesn't seem too promising now," Tom said, as he drooped his head in despair.

"You mean that you would help humans, too, even the mean ones?" asked Randall, jumping down from the edge of the bowl. "Yes, I suppose I would, everything on this green earth deserves a sendoff," replied Tom. Randall stood tall on his hairy legs, his antennae pointing directly at Tom's nose. He pronounced, with complete admiration in his voice, "That's a fine idea, and a noble, worthwhile ambition. Tom, my boy, you want to be an Angel Cat!"

CHAPTER FOUR:
The Flood

"If it doesn't stop raining soon, we're gonna be in a lot of trouble around here," announced Bart, as he looked out the dirty window.

"Yep, the creek is rising more every day; I sure hope we don't flood again. It's too much trouble and work moving all these animals—we might just do them a favor by leaving them here," said Hazel.

"How would *you* like to be left behind caged up in a flood, knowing there was no way to escape your fate?" asked Ollie. "That was a pretty mean and cruel thing to say, Hazel, even for you," Bart added.

"Well, if the City doesn't care about fixing the problem, and the public can't give us enough money for a new shelter for their abandoned pets, it sounds like a right good idea to me, mean-sounding or not," she replied.

Randall, who was lounging on the reception desk, took in this whole conversation, and eyed them with disgust. "Humans should be brought back as cats and dogs, or even bugs, to see what life is like for stray animals, or running for your life from fly-swatters and a big can of Raid," he thought to himself. Scurrying into Tom's cell to give him the daily gossip report, he barely avoided a fatal squish from Hazels' humongous foot.

"Can you hear them talking, Tom? They say it might flood again! We lost a lot of animals in the '85 flood, a bunch of my kin, and friends too, such a bad business that was. "

"Randall, I'm too depressed to worry about a rain storm or a creek. I'm going on my next-to-last day here; nobody's gonna save me anyway, so I might as well drown. At least Hazel and Bart won't get the pleasure of watching me expire," Tom said forlornly. "Cheer up, fellow," Randall said, in between bites of cat chow. "You got nine lives, right?"

"I don't know. Neither Sheba nor Miss Opal ever said anything about nine lives. I think my inner voice may have mentioned it, but I'm screwed then, because I've never been real good at counting," replied Tom with a perplexed look on his face.

That night the rain came down harder and harder, making pinging noises on the tin roof and splat-splat sounds as it hit the decayed tiles on the floor of Tom's cell through the cracks in the ceiling. Tom, increasingly nervous, paced back and forth in his cage. The night seemed to go on forever. He could hear the other animals howling in fear in the distant rooms, louder all the time.

Daylight finally broke, and Bart and Ollie entered the room for their early-morning rounds. "Breakfast time," said Ollie cheerfully.

"Now, Ollie, you have too much food with you; we must do what Hazel said and give him only half-portions today," said Bart.

"Even prisoners on Death Row get a good last meal; this just don't seem right to me." But Ollie gave in, and Tom received a very small portion of dry food, and no clean water. The two of them left the room, joking between themselves about how Hazel had fallen on her butt in the mud coming into work that morning.

"Lord, if you have a plan for me, could you just hurry it up a bit? I know that I am probably way down on your to-do list; just don't forget about me, please, amen," prayed Tom under his breath. He looked at his breakfast, but he didn't feel very hungry. A deep sadness had enveloped his soul, and he laid down to watch the rain still coming down in sheets, pelting his lone window. "Might as well take a nap, got to keep up my strength."

Tom slept for a good while, dreaming of all the happy times he'd had with Dinkles, Miss Opal and Sheba. Lazy days laying in the sun, hours exploring his world, minutes chasing Dinkles, the warmth of Sheba's tail when he was a kitten, and Miss Opal's loving hand on his head as he lay on the front porch.

Thunder crashed so loud that it rattled Tom's cage, and the lightning lit up the room, startling him from his nap. The noise from the other rooms was deafening, as the other animals started to panic; it seemed everyone's nerves were at a breaking point.

The room had gone almost black as the thunderstorm boomed on. "Where in the world is Randall—I could use a good friend to talk to right about now," Tom thought. He could hear bits and pieces of panicked talk among the other animals—how the shelter was going to flood, and how frightened they were.

"Some of those guys could be my old friends from the neighborhood, but I hope not," he said to himself.

Tom almost wept in relief as Randall finally appeared from under Tom's cage door. "What do you want, Tom?" he asked.

"You've got to help me get out of here today," cried Tom, finally breaking down into tears.

"Do *what*? Are you insane, Tom? Me and what army?" asked Randall in disbelief. "That's just it! I know that you're not the only cockroach in this joint. Call all your cousins, aunts and uncles, tell them it's gonna be a jail break today!" announced Tom excitedly. "Here comes Hazel, so get going, and be careful," he whispered. Randall made tracks quickly to avoid the fly-swatter Hazel always carried with her in case she encountered his kind.

"What a wonderful day it is, all dark and gloomy. If I recollect correctly, Mr. Tomcat, this is your last day in this-here establishment; you've got no prospects for adoption at all," she chuckled as she waddled into the room. "Bart, bring me that clipboard."

"You gonna sign off on this paperwork right now? It's not the end of the day yet," Bart said.

"You better believe I am. It gives me great pleasure to sign off on this waste of space," she answered.

"All humans can't possibly be this mean; Miss Sally and Miss Opal weren't, but of course they were the only other real humans I have ever been close to, or known at all well," thought Tom.

Finally, the gruesome twosome left Tom alone to ponder his fate. "Never fear, Randall is here," Tom heard the little cockroach-y voice behind him. "Well, here's the crew, just like you asked for," said Randall. Following behind him were hundreds of cockroaches of every size in a perfectly straight line that seemed to stretch on forever.

"Randall, aren't you scared?" asked Tom, starting to shake at the thought of Hazel catching them in the act.

"Nope. We cockroaches are superbugs, didn't you know that? The only thing we're afraid of is a larger-than-life can of Raid (by the way, we don't talk much about that, it brings bad luck)," laughed Randall. "Let me introduce you to my aunt and uncle. Tom, this is my Aunt Viv and my Uncle Cecil," he said with an air of respect.

"Nice to meet you, Tom. We never thought that we would be helping out a cat; our breed usually runs from them," said Uncle Cecil.

"We brought the whole family to help," chimed in Aunt Viv. "Any friend of Randall's is a friend of ours," they remarked in unison. Tom's eyes welled with tears as he extended his paw to Uncle Cecil's many appendages in a weird kind of handshake.

"On my cat's honor, with the Lord as witness, I will never chase or eat another cockroach again," he announced.

"Enough of that gooey stuff; we have work to do," said Randall. "Where are Baby Susie and Sweetpea?" whispered Aunt Viv. "Here we are," replied the two smallest cockroaches in the bunch.

"You two little ones must crawl into the cage and into the lock on the door, and try to work the levers back and forth, while the rest of us work on the hinges that connect the door to the cage," instructed Uncle Cecil. "Randall, you and some of your cousins guard the door and give us a shout-out if you see anybody coming this way," he commanded with a general's air. "Petey and Boo, you two work on loosening up the bars," said Aunt Viv in her dainty voice. "All together now, let's get started," shouted Uncle Cecil.

Tom sat back and stared in amazement as Randall and his whole family worked feverishly to make him a free cat. "You guys need to hurry up, because fat ol' Hazel is always on time, and Bart and Ollie will be tagging along with her today," shouted Randall. "I think we got it!" said Baby Susie and Sweetpea simultaneously, antennae twitching a hundred miles an hour.

"Petey and Boo, you two pull as hard as you can on that door," said Uncle Cecil.

Tom helped, too, gently pushing with his paw from the inside. "It's open, the door is open! Tom, you are now a free cat!" shouted the whole family.

Freedom had never felt so good or so sweet, thought Tom. "I could never have done this without your help and the help of your family, Randall; I will always be indebted to you and yours for this and future generations," he said to his good new friend.

Before all the hugs, kisses and congrats could go around, the air was filled with the sound of horns and sirens. A tremendous "boom!" caused Tom to leap from his newly opened cage and run right in between Hazel's legs as she entered the room.

"The river has crested, run for your lives," shouted Randall. Hazel stood transfixed as the water began to cover her shoes.

"Where is the orange tabby, Hazel?" asked Ollie as he burst into the room.

"Don't worry about that mangy cat; he's escaped, and I hope he drowns. We have to get the other animals out of here, the ones worth saving, the money-makers for the shelter," she shouted angrily.

"Water is everywhere. I *hate* water! Where do I go? Why, up a tree, of course," Tom thought, as he scrambled for safety. The sights and smells of the great outdoors assaulted Tom's senses.

"Freedom, sweet freedom is the best, but I never figured I'd have to swim to find it again," he said out loud.

He swam through the parking lot until he found a sturdy-looking tree branch at the river's edge. Pulling himself up with all his might, he perched upon it, clinging with all four paws, nails embedded deeply. Soaking wet, with droplets of water falling from his whiskers, he watched as a crowd of volunteers rushed to save the animals still trapped inside their kennels.

The sky was almost pitch-black, like deepest night, and the roar of the rushing water and booms of thunder were deafening, and streaks of lightening made sizzling noises as they struck trees along the riverbank, cracking some of them in half.

Tom clung desperately onto the crooked branch just inches above the swirling water. Bobbing and weaving in each strong gust of wind, he watched dozens of firefighters, police officers and volunteers braving the strong currents of Tinker Creek now engulfing the shelter, rescuing the other animals, sometimes two at a time, from their certain watery death. The scene that was unfolding before him seemed like a make-believe movie, an action-filled rockem' sockem' thriller like those he and Miss Opal used to watch.

In an instant, Tom was brought out of his daze by the most frightened meow that he had ever heard. Coming toward him, waving its paws futilely, its head barely above the brown swirling water, was what appeared to be a baby kitten on the verge of going under for the last time.

He could see that the kitten was swallowing way too much water; his pitiful meow was a bit weaker as he drew nearer. "Go ahead, Tom, you know what you must do," he heard a voice in his head tell him.

Without hesitation, he jumped into the ice-cold, debris-filled current and shouted to the struggling kitten, "Climb onto my back, hold on tight and don't let go!" As the kitten, utterly exhausted, pulled itself onto Tom's back, Tinker Creek took them both quickly downstream. Hanging on for dear life, the kitten dug its tiny claws into Tom's strong back muscles.

Tom swam toward the nearest bank, fighting the strong currents and trying to dodge tree limbs as they rushed by. His lungs felt like they were about to burst, and with his last good breath, he managed to shout above the din to the kitten, "Just a little way more!" as he felt the last of his strength giving way.

"Pastor Green, over this way, quick, over here!" shouted one of the volunteers.

Pastor Green heard the shouts, and came running with the largest net he had. "It's one of the cats, he's in the river, he needs help, looks like something's clinging to his back—please hurry with your net!" yelled the lady volunteer. Pastor Green and several volunteers from the local VA Center hospital had come to help rescue the shelter animals. The pastor had always been an animal-lover, and kept up with the goings-on at the shelter. When he heard on the local radio station that the creek was to crest that morning, he gathered up as many men and women from his neighborhood as he could, and high-tailed it to the northeast side of town.

"Nurse Betty, I'll hold onto that big tree limb by wrapping my legs around it, and when I'm safely up there, you hand me the net," shouted the pastor. He made his way to the end of the large branch jutting over the rushing water, and lay down, hoping that the limb would hold his weight. "Hand me the net now!" he yelled to the nurse. He swept the net through the rushing waters, and on his second try he swooped up Tom and his rider. "Gotcha," hollered the pastor. Up into the air went Tom and the kitten, all bundled up together in the huge net, dangling over the creek as the pastor inched his way backwards on the tree limb to safety.

Shouts of joy surrounded them all, as dozens of onlookers lined the creek bank to witness the daring rescue.

"Let's get these guys to higher ground," said a volunteer firefighter named Billy.

Across his back went the net with Tom and the kitten, who was still hanging onto Tom's back, but now very weakly. Even though Tom was upside down, he could see people everywhere—carrying cages, dragging frightened dogs on leashes, and cradling cats in their arms, making for higher ground.

They trudged up the hill behind the shelter. Billy gently laid the net down upon a blanket that had been spread out on the ground for the most severely injured animals. Doc Williams, who worked at the VA hospital, but on occasion volunteered at the animal shelter, began to untangle Tom and the kitten, who was still attached to Tom's back, from the net. Tom, limp and exhausted, didn't have the strength to stand and shake the water from his fur. He was patted down with a towel by Nurse Betty. His golden eyes glistened with tears as he looked into baby kitten's green eyes so full of fear, and saw its breathing so very shallow. "You're gonna be all right, little friend," he whispered.

Billy picked Tom up and put him in a cage set by the blanket's edge, so that Doc Williams would have room to work on the small gray kitten. "Hey, Doc, how are the two cats from the river doing?" asked Pastor Green, making his way over to the sick-area. "The big orange tabby is going to be okay, but the kitten, I think, has swallowed too much water, and his heartbeat is not strong, either; he may have been in bad health before all of this drama; so much strain on such a little heart," replied the doctor.

On hearing this prognosis, Tom gathered his strength and stood up. He commenced to make the biggest commotion he could by banging against the cage, meowing loudly and chewing at the latch. "Seems to me that ol' orange cat wants out real bad, for some reason," said Doc. "Let him out then, and let's see what he does," said the pastor.

"Thank you Lord, they understood me," said Tom to himself.

Doc Williams lifted the latch and the door swung open. Tom sprang past him to the baby kitten's side. He lay himself very gently on top of the kitten, making sure he didn't put all of his weight on him. Into the kitten's ear Tom softly said, "Don't be afraid, my little buddy, you are going to a beautiful place called animal heaven, where you can run and play to your heart's content, catch all the bugs and mice you want, and nap all day in fields of sweet-smelling clover. The sun will shine on you, and there will be no cares or worries, ever again. I'll stay here with you until your journey begins; you won't be alone, and God will lift you up gently above me to show you the way. I will be watching and praying for your safe and peaceful release," he whispered.

"Well, it seems this little fellow isn't gonna make it," the Doc said to everyone gathered near the blanket. Pastor Green, a somewhat larger-than-life-size man, looking more like a boxer than a Baptist preacher, pulled out his old white handkerchief to wipe away the tears that had begun to form in his eyes. Doc Williams, the total opposite of the pastor, was a small, wiry gentleman with a weather-beaten complexion and thinning silver hair that seemed to spring from different places on his unusually large head.

He started to cough and shuffle his bony legs around to cover up his emotions.

Oblivious to the two men's conversation, Tom concentrated on the baby kitten's eyes. In those eyes, shone trust, love, and a deep gratitude for not being left alone. One so-small meow escaped the kitten's mouth as his eyes shut for the last time. "Into God's arms you go, little one," whispered Tom. Looking skyward, he watched the baby kitten floating above him, jumping with joy. One last look between them, and then the kitten was engulfed by the most bright and sparkling light Tom had ever witnessed; then the kitten was gone. "Godspeed, baby kitten," he meowed softly.

"Guess what, everybody, we managed to get all of the animals to safety, thanks to all the valley volunteers and you folks," Ollie shouted, as he and Bart ran up the hill to the triage area. "What's that orange tabby doing all the way up here, anyway? He looks a sight, even worse than before," said Bart.

"Well, gentlemen, you are looking at quite the hero, yes, sir, you are. This big tomcat jumped into Tinker Creek and carried a little gray kitten to safety," replied Pastor Green. "But to no avail, I'm afraid; the kitten was in poor health before all this happened—he had only the tiniest chance of living," Doc added.

Hazel, huffing and puffing, trying to make her way up the steep hill, overheard the group's discussion of Tom's heroism, and stopped just short of the two men.

Looking down on Tom with her hands on her hips, red hair completely frazzled, she took one big breath, and announced, "Don't matter anyway, should've been him that passed.

His time's up today, needle to the leg this one has coming, hero or no hero."

All the men and women stood in stunned silence, trying to absorb the sheer unfeelingness of her announcement.

"Look, the rains stopped, the thunderstorm is over," said the pastor, bringing the group out of their contemplation over Tom's imminent demise. "There's a rainbow, too," shouted a volunteer. Dozens of people yelled and cheered, men and women slapped and patted each other on the back for a job well done. Both humans and animals knew that the worst was over.

"Hey, Tomcat, over here," whispered Randall. Tom sat up and looked to his left.

At the blanket's edge was Randall and his whole family peeking out between the blades of grass. "We all made it Tom; glad to see you made it, too. What happened here, my friend?" he asked.

"It's a long story, Randall, and I'm too worn out to go into it right now. Someday I'll tell you all about it," he replied.

"Man, all these humans are making me nervous; there are just too many feet around here," chuckled Randall. "We're off to the store down the street.

I've got some kinfolks that are gonna put us up for awhile; we're all gonna stay at the store. There's lots of good eating there, I hear. Where are you off to, Tom?"

"I don't have a clue, but according to Hazel, I'm a gonner," Tom replied.

"If you want, me and the family will crawl up her ol' fat legs and scare her away—or better yet, we could make her fall into the creek! Don't worry, she won't drown, she'll only float," joked Randall. The whole family burst into laughter, antennae giving high- fives.

"No thanks, buddy, that wouldn't solve my problem," sighed Tom. "I want to thank you and your family for being such good friends, and just in case I never see you or your kin again, please take care of yourselves. This I promise you, Randall, I'll never let anyone say bad things about your kind again," he promised, as he carefully patted Randall on the head. "So long, Tomcat, we're off," the family said in unison as they marched away in single file into the woods and towards the store.

Tom looked up at all the people surrounding him. "These humans are deciding my future right now," he thought. And with that thought still fresh in his mind, he let out a series of the most heart-wrenching meows ever witnessed by animal or human. His eyes closed, he put his head back, and his meows got louder and louder. Cat-tears were flowing, a cat's prayer for sure.

"That cat must be touched in the head, all that caterwalling" remarked Hazel, as she uneasily stepped back away from Tom. "God-awful sound, if you ask me," Doc Williams agreed covering his ears.

As suddenly as he'd started, Tom stopped crying, opened his eyes, and focused his entire attention on Pastor Green's face. They stared at each other for what seemed like an eternity. Then Tom, exhausted from his ordeal and certain now of his fate, sat down and started to groom himself from top to bottom, as if nothing had happened, feeling completely content with his world.

"You guys okay up there?" yelled Mr. Bedwell, the director of the animal shelter. Taking huge, long strides up the hill at a fast pace, the young man with the full black beard and hair to match reached the group in a matter of moments. "Just to let you know, we've found temporary homes for all the shelter animals, and I really want to thank each one of you from the VA hospital for your help," he said, as he extended his hand for shakes all around. "I don't know what we would have done without all you guys and gals. If there's anything I or my team can ever do for you to help repay this kindness, please let me know,"

Brought back into the conversation among the people standing around him, Tom heard the words he had been waiting to hear seemingly forever.

"Actually, there is something you can do for us. The Palliative Care Unit of the Veterans Affairs Center hospital would like to adopt this cat, as of right now!" announced Pastor Green in an upraised voice like the one he used for preaching on Sundays.

"Done," replied Mr. Bedwell, with a grin on his face.

CHAPTER FIVE:

The Hospital

Tom took one last look at the baby kitten before they covered him up. Pastor Green and Doc put Tom in a dark blue, soft-sided pet carrier and slid him into the back of the hospital's van.

"A whole new adventure awaits me; I wonder what it's going to be like to live in a hospital?" he thought to himself, as he enjoyed his clean and spacious new digs. "And just what *is* a hospital, anyway?" he wondered.

"Here we are, buddy, we're home," said Pastor Green, as he stopped the van in front of the biggest brick building that Tom had ever seen. As Tom, in his carrier, emerged from the back of the van, as far as his eyes could see were rows and rows of red-brick buildings with tall white columns and large front porches. He saw open, grassy areas dotted with majestic old oak trees. A fountain with cool and refreshing water spouted from a serene marble angel surrounded by a flower bed of deep-wine colored roses, swarming with honey bees and multicolored butterflies. "A wondrous place, filled with the Lord's creations. I've never seen a place so beautiful," thought Tom.

Humans were everywhere: walking, running, in cars from which horns of different tones were honking simultaneously. It seemed to Tom like a complete city all its own.

Pastor Green and Doc Williams toted Tom through a large double door that magically opened by itself.

"Eh mon, what you have there, mon?" asked the tallest and strangest-sounding human Tom had ever seen or heard. His skin was black as night, and his hair, also black, looked like a thousand snakes jutting from his head.

"Domingo, my friend, I would like to introduce you to our newest staff member. His name is Tom," Doc Williams said. "Tom, this is Domingo. He'll be taking care of you sometimes, along with other good people who work here," said Doc, handing the carrier over into Domingo's care. As Domingo extended his hand for Tom to sniff, Tom caught the scent that he was too familiar with, one which disturbed him, yet didn't make him afraid. Because Tom was a genuine alley cat from the streets, he came upon that smell often on sick or injured animals. It was the same scent baby kitten had had, and when he recognized it and accepted it, he licked Domingo's hand.

"It seems, Domingo, that you have a way with cats, the same way you do with the women in this place," laughed the pastor.

"Na, na mon, you be akidding me; this little mon here already much nicer than the ladies," Domingo said, with a mischievous grin on his face.

"Take him up to the third floor Palliative Care Ward, please, and leave him in my office for now. We'll come up with a plan for his stay here later," said Pastor Green to Domingo.

Domingo took charge of Tom and carried him a few feet to another set of double gray doors. He used just one finger to push something round on the wall, and to Tom's surprise, the doors slid into the sides of the wall, with a loud clanging noise.

Tom, still carried by Domingo, entered the small room, which jerked and swayed in a curious manner. Tom felt a bit sick from the motion.

"First elevator ride, eh, mon?" Domingo asked, grinning as he peered into Tom's carrier, which was now splattered with the remains of the supper he'd had the night before. "Strange contraptions these humans have," thought Tom to himself. "How do they manage to keep on their feet in here, and keep their dinners, too!"

The elevator doors opened and Domingo, with Tom in tow, stepped out onto a brand- new floor. "Well, me cat-friend, this is your new abode, and just so you know who's who, the guys in the long white coats are doctors, and the lovely ladies in their scrubs the different shades of the rainbow are nurses," instructed Domingo.

Tom, eyes gone wide in awe, began to take in all the sights and sounds and smells around him as Domingo carried him down the long hallway. Everywhere he looked were humans, some driving two-wheeled contraptions. Attached to some of them were long, skinny poles that supported clear bags full of some kind of liquid. Each room he passed contained a human, either in a bed or sitting in one of those electric chairs. Some were sleeping; some were just staring into space, not paying any attention to the blaring TV sets. As the man and the cat drew nearer to the end of the hallway, they passed a set of three empty rooms, all on the right side of the hallway.

A very quiet calm descended upon Tom as he passed these rooms, and he instinctively knew that they contained a spiritual presence that gave him the feeling of loving arms wrapped around him.

"Here you are, my mon, the pastor's office," said Domingo, as he set the carrier down and unzipped the door just enough to clean up Tom's accident with a rag from his pocket. "I'll leave you be now, my mon, so you can rest," he said over his shoulder as he left the room. Tom finally felt able to relax, and managed to give himself a good once-over licking. He curled up into a ball, head tucked under his belly, and purred himself to sleep.

He awoke from his nap to an annoying buzzing sound close to his ear, which he swatted at with one paw, hoping to stop the irritating noise.

"Watch it, bozo!" said the fattest and ugliest black fly he had ever encountered. "You almost got me!"

Tom turned around in his carrier to get a better look at this pest with the multi-faceted eyeballs staring a hole through him. "Who are you?" asked Tom, as the fly lit upon his nose.

"Festus, at your service, Mr. Tomcat. I am the Official Resident Fly, and I also do messenger service, if needed. And what, dear sir, is your branch of military service, if I may inquire?"

"To tell the truth, Festus, I'm just an alley cat that used to live in the streets of the City," said Tom.

"Ah, I understand, you are kinda like a ground trooper fighting in a concrete jungle.

I come from a long line of military flies, myself; serving our country is a family tradition," remarked Festus, puffing out his chest with pride.

"Festus, it's nice to meet you. My name is Tom," he said, yawning.

"What's your story, Tom?" asked the fly.

"My story is a long one; Pastor Green and some other folks rescued me from the flood today, and from certain death, as I was next in line for Hazel's revenge."

"Who's Hazel?" asked Festus, as he buzzed around and around in circles above Tom's head.

"She was the warden at the animal shelter in the valley, where I'd been taken after Ollie and Bart caught me on the streets, where I'd been hiding," Tom answered.

"Why did you live on the streets? Didn't you have a real, inside home?"

"I used to live with a very nice old lady named Miss Opal, but she got sick, and Mr. Plunkett kicked me out," answered Tom with a sad tone in his voice.

Festus decided to light on the inside of the mesh window of the carrier because it was half unzipped and it made such a nice landing spot. He wanted to get a better look at Tom as he retold his long journey from the cruel world to the hospital.

And so they talked for a long time–it seemed like hours–until Festus felt that he had gotten enough information to distribute the juicy gossip to the entire ward about its new resident cat.

Tom pushed down the carrier window so that he could stick out his head and look around; still a bit skittish, he didn't want to exit completely.

"Tell me, Festus, what is that red, white, and blue thing hanging on that pole in the corner?"

"That's the American flag, for goodness sake, I thought everybody knew that," Festus replied. "It represents our country and freedom; lots of men and women have died defending that symbol, because it means even an ol' fly like I am can do what I want, live where I want, and pray or not pray if I want," answered Festus proudly. "Don't you know, you silly cat, that you're in a military hospital, where soldiers young and old come for help, some to pass their final years in dignity before they leave this world; that's what this ward is for. You're on the Palliative Care Ward, Tom," said Festus. Tom nodded his head in understanding, as Festus took flight toward the open doorway.

Tom glanced around the office; it looked nice and comfy, like Miss Opal's house. There were pictures on the wall, a handsome rug on the floor, and warm sunshine streamed in through an open window. He felt content, at peace with the world, and as if he were home at last.

His attention was caught by something in the hallway, and he turned around in his carrier to face the right direction. He overheard Festus talking. "I think that he understands that Pastor Green and all the doctors and nurses on this ward take care of the terminally ill veterans, and that we treat them and their families with respect, and we comfort them before they pass over," said Festus.

"Veterans take care of their own. This is a blessed place for these people, some of whom don't have any family at all, so we're their family now," said an unfamiliar voice.

Before Tom could digest all that he had heard, Festus had breezed right in and landed upside down on the pastor's lampshade.

"So, Festus, since you seem to be the one with all the information and opinions around this place, why do think Pastor Green brought me here?" asked Tom.

"Don't know for sure, but I'll find, out" Festus replied. "Ever heard the old saying, 'I wish I was a fly on the wall'? Well, guess what–it's true, and I am that fly," he laughed. "I hear the pastor coming now, so it's time to make my rounds. I'll see you in a bit," he said, as he headed for the open door.

"Isn't he adorable," cooed a petite, blonde woman, as she poked her finger into the carrier to stroke Tom's back. "My name is Katie, and we are going to be the best of friends from now on," she said.

"Let me look at him. Well, he's a bit on the scrawny side, and smelly too," said a large lady with an olive complexion.

The pastor, who was the last one to enter his office, caught this final remark. "True, Maude, but not all heroes are fat and sassy," he chuckled.

"I'll fatten him up and give him a good scrubbing, too; he'll be smelling like a rose," said Maude, as she peered into the carrier and held her nose at the same time.

"Oh, he doesn't smell *that* bad, Maude," said the orderly on call for the day, a tall, lanky lad with a mop of curly brown hair, named Jacob.

"Pastor Green, correct me if I'm wrong, but didn't you say that this cat has had a rough time of it, and that he was some kind of hero who tried to save a kitten from drowning, or something?"

"You're correct, Jacob; he has been sorely mistreated, and he *is* a hero. That's why I feel he is a special cat, and one well worth saving," answered the pastor lovingly.

The pastor pulled Tom out of his carrier and cradled him in his arms. "Okay, everybody, let's get a plan together for how we're gonna take care of this cat—and, by the way, his name is Tom," he added.

"Since I'm the one in charge of delivering the food trays for each meal, and the sweet young thing in the kitchen has a little crush on me, I think that I can talk her into special treats on the days we have chicken, and on fish-Fridays," said Jacob.

"And I will fix him up a nice place to sleep. Maybe we can use the spare bathroom at the end of the hall," chimed in Katie.

"Thank you all for your offers to help; it'll take us all to take good care of him, because Tom has a mission here. He might not know what it is yet, but he will, sooner or later," remarked the pastor.

Katie gently laid Tom down on the small green love seat next to the window, and gave him stern orders to not go to the bathroom on anything in the room.

"I'll be back in a jiffy, to show you to your very own residence," said Katie excitedly. Maude and Ethel, the two head nurses on duty for the day, looked at each other, and both spoke at the same time. "Rounds first, and bath and de-fleaing second," and everyone laughed.

Tom, oblivious to the whole conversation, was in the midst of a serious scratching session, trying to catch the little black boogers, as he called them, that tormented him on a continuous basis.

"Excellent, excellent, I knew I could count on you folks to show a good team effort on behalf of our newest staff member," chuckled the pastor.

Tom, totally exhausted from his losing battle with the fleas, gave up and rolled onto his back and purred himself back to sleep, never hearing the door close softly as the group left the room.

"Let's all get back to work; we're got lots of veterans to attend to. I'll page Domingo back to the ward to help you, Jacob, and you can give him instructions on what we need in order to make Tom a place of his own," Maude said in her commander's voice.

"And I must not be late for my meeting, because I have to explain to the higher-ups just why I brought a cat back from the shelter to live in this hospital," shouted Pastor Green, as he ran to catch the elevator. "God be with me, this will be a hard sell, indeed," he thought to himself.

Festus, having witnessed all of this commotion and having been privy to the entire conversation from his vantage point on the nurses' station computer, wasted no time in reporting back to his cousins and his fly-friends the new developments.

So eager was he, he didn't look where he was heading and bumbled smack into another of the hospital's flies.

"Sorry about bonking into you, Tizzy, but I was kind of in a hurry," he said. "You do remember what I told you about Tom the Cat—and did you hear all the rest?" he asked.

"Sure, I remember; I do have eyes and antennae, you know. I think he'll be a great addition to our big family," said Tizzy, a little sarcastically.

"I'm headed to the second floor, as soon as someone gets off the elevator, to tell Bird and his crew all the juicy details about how Tom the Cat wound up here," Festus said, as he flew down the hall to the elevator and landed on the down-button.

"Yes, you go right ahead and tell Bird and his fancy, better-than-thou friends all about it; I bet he'll be thrilled to know that there's a cat running around here," chuckled

Tizzy, as she lit on the ceiling light fixture at the elevator doors. "A lot of fuss about nothing, if you ask me, all these humans buzzing around here willy-nilly, excited about an old cat, huh!" she thought to herself as she bumped into the next light fixture.

Tom awoke refreshed and very hungry. He surveyed the office, hoping to catch a glimpse of some food or water. Spying a green plant on the windowsill, he made his way with just two leaps from the love seat to the old pine desk, scattering papers everywhere, and to the window. He tipped over a vase as he tried to get a drink from it, and caused it to fall to the floor with a loud crash.

Giving up on the idea of eating or drinking, he thought, "Not such a good start to my new life here," and he lay down to catch the breeze and feel the warm sunshine coming through the open window.

"Good morning, Tom," said Pastor Green, as he entered his office, ready for a new day's work. "I can tell by the big mess in here that you've been very busy exploring," he remarked, gathering up his papers from the floor.

"We must hide this broken vase, because it belongs to Maude; she'll throw a fit if she sees it," he said, as he scooped up the broken glass. "I'll bet you're hungry, thirsty, and in need of a bathroom break after having slept a whole day and night, so come with me, Tom, and I'll show you to your new quarters."

Tom jumped from the windowsill and followed him into the hallway, weaving in and out of the pastor's legs to let him know that, yes, he was starved, and in need of a toilet, quickly. They stopped in front of a tiny room not far from the pastor's office, and he said, "Tom, this is your new home. See the sign above the door? It reads 'Tom's House.'"

Tom glanced up at the sign made of wood, hanging kind of lopsided by a string, and thought to himself, I must be dreaming. "Go on in, buddy, you have all the creature comforts of a real home, including a litter box; I do hope you know how to use a litter box?" asked Pastor Green, with a concerned look on his face. "Maybe I should inspect my office, after all," he said worriedly, as he hurried back down the hall.

My, Tom was annoyed. "Listen, fellow, I am not just any ol' alley cat; I do have some upbringing and manners, thanks to Miss Opal, of course," he said.

"Now, just where in the world is that cat?" yelled Maude, as she came down the hall toward the pastor's office. "He is in his cat place, Maude," shouted back the pastor.

"Good grief—she sure caught me in an awkward position," Tom mumbled, as Maude stood in the doorway watching him use the litter box.

"Mr. Tom, you come with me right now. I'm going to show you how to find your way around here, and introduce you to the other staff members and some of the patients. Come on, kitty, kitty," she said in a high childish voice.

Tom looked up at Maude with utter disdain. "I am a fairly intelligent cat, and I can understand the human language quite well, so I might as well show what I know," he figured, as he gave out a loud meow. He followed her down the hallway to the nurses' station, making sure he didn't get run over by all the traffic on the way. The hall was filled with every condition of human and wheelchair you could imagine. The noise level was intense, almost as bad as the freeway that he used to have to cross at home. "Weaving in and out of this traffic, a body could lose a tail," thought Tom.

"Hey buddy, where you headed to?" asked Festus as he flew overhead, and with the precision of a jet bomber landed on Tom's left ear. "To meet and greet," Tom answered, as he bumped into Maude's enormous legs when she stopped abruptly. The impact knocked Festus over. "Like hitting a pair of tree trunks," said Festus, as he righted himself.

Katie and Domingo were standing behind the station where Maude stopped first. "You already know these guys, so just you stay here with them for a while, because I hear a buzzer going off in Mr. Deacon's room," she said, hurrying down the hall. Tom jumped up on the desk and made himself comfortable, Festus still onboard.

"Just look at him, Ethel, and you too, Domingo, isn't he the most precious thing you have ever seen?" asked Katie as she rubbed all the right spots on his neck. Tom arched his back and purred as Katie, Ethel and Domingo fussed over him. He decided to stay just where he was and lay back down to watch his new friends do their job.

It was a traffic nightmare—lights and buzzers were going off every which way, and people in white coats or scrubs were in and out of rooms, chatting about different patients.

Tom watched Ethel, a small, wrinkled, white-haired nurse with kind eyes, rummage around in a large brown paper bag. "I think I have all the supplies I'll need," she said, looking straight at Tom. "Mr. Tomcat, Maude called me into work early today because she's made me responsible for giving you your bath and flea dip this morning," she stated matter-of-factly. "Tell Maude when she comes back that we are on our mission to make this kitty presentable," she told Katie and Domingo.

Ethel picked me up, cradled me in her arms along with her brown bag, and started toward the elevator.

As we passed the different rooms, she explained to me what they were: First we saw the patients' dayroom, used for entertainment and social events with the veterans' families.

"All the other rooms are occupied by very special patients, each one a veteran of the different branches of the service. They served their country with pride and dignity, and they come here to spend their last remaining days," she explained to Tom. "We take care of them, no matter what their illness, to show our appreciation for their contributions to their country, and we must treat them with great love and respect at all times," she whispered into Tom's ear, batting Festus off as she did so.

Jacob was sitting on the couch across from the elevator reading a magazine. As they approached, he said, "Ethel, check out the sign on the elevator doors: I made it myself!"

The sign, burned into a wooden plaque, read "Be Aware of Cat."

"Great idea, Jacob, now the people coming or going will be on the lookout for Tom," she said, "and we hope they won't be letting him take himself on unsupervised rides. Tom, you must never get on this elevator by yourself, and that's an order. You could get lost, and that would be a cat-astrophe," she said sternly.

"Need some help with all that stuff?" asked Jacob, as he reached for the brown bag.

"Yes, thank you; I'm off to give Tom a very-much-needed bath," she said as the elevator doors opened. Tom thought that he understood what Ethel meant by getting lost, and he also knew from living on the streets that a bunch of folks didn't like cats at all. He also understood that, somehow, Pastor Green was responsible for him and his whereabouts, and he didn't want to cause him any trouble. He licked Ethel's arm in hopes that she'd know he had understood her.

The elevator dinged and the doors opened onto the first floor of the hospital. "This place is gigantic; just look at all these chairs lined up on either side of this long, cavernous room! It seems to go on forever, and, oh, the huge skylights above letting in the bright sunlight I love, though there are too many humans for my taste," thought Tom.

They passed through swinging doors into what Jacob told him was the rehab center. Ethel deposited Tom into an extra-large wash basin, where Jacob held him still.

After a less-than-gentle scrubbing, and an entire bottle of flea shampoo later, Ethel wrapped him in a soft, fluffy towel, and they carried him, fast asleep, back upstairs, gently placing him on the new cat-cushion that Jacob had arranged in his carrier. Careful not to wake him, they both tiptoed out, leaving him in his new home.

The aroma of fresh-fried chicken wafted past Tom's nose, making it twitch.

Waves of hunger pains woke him. He found himself in his house, its open flap facing a juicy bowl of mouth-watering chicken chunks. He yawned, took a quick stretch, and padded over to his dinner bowl to enjoy his meal.

"Tom, my boy, up here," called Festus from his perch on the sink above Tom's head, cleaning his wings after having helped himself to Tom's meal while he slept. "When you've finished your dinner, we must go on a meet-and-greet tour of the ward, which you didn't accomplish earlier, and I'll introduce you to all the patients here; you're quite the talk of the ward right now," said Festus.

As soon as Tom had consumed every last morsel in his bowl, then licked it clean a couple of times, he began his ritual of grooming himself, whiskers first and tail last, as all cats do. "I'm ready now, Festus, so hop onto my back and we'll take this famous tour of yours."

Because it was later in the day, the hallway had cleared out to a reasonable degree, and the pair started their walk in relative safety.

"First stop, Tom, will be Mr. Deacon's room," said Festus, as he tried to ignore Tom's constant stopping to mark his territory with a wiggle of his tail. Tom stopped just inside of the threshold to take a look-see. The room contained all the things he had glimpsed earlier in the day. It had a bed, a table with a lamp and a television set, a few chairs, and a floor-to-ceiling wardrobe lining one wall.

The curtains at the only window were of the fanciest white lace, just like Miss Opal used to have. It all made Tom feel homesick for just a few seconds. The man in the bed was asleep, and Tom, with Festus riding on his collar now, jumped onto the bed to get a better look. The fly commenced to fill the cat in on the man under the covers pulled up to his chin, who was snoring like a freight train.

"Mr. Deacon was in the army, and he walks with a cane; he's here because he has a bad heart," he informed Tom. "Tizzy told me she overheard Pastor Green and Maude talking the other day, and they said Mr. Deacon might not make it to Christmastime," he continued, as he flew about and landed on Mr. Deacon's cane. Tom laid down at the bottom of the bed to survey the frail old man and crossed his paws to say a prayer for him. Gently, then, so as not to wake the sleeping man, he jumped down to the floor, motioning for Festus to follow him.

"Hey, you two, up here," yelled Tizzy as she buzzed her continuous journey from one light fixture to the next. "Cat, since we haven't been formally introduced, my name is Tizzy, and I can tell you the real deal about Mr. Deacon" said the moth.

"He suffers from what Maude calls dementia; he forgets things, so don't feel bad if he doesn't remember who you are five minutes after he meets you. On some days he still thinks he's in the army and may tell you to stand at attention," said Tizzy.

"Yeah, and if he throws his food at you, then you know that to him, it's k.p. duty day," laughed Festus. "Also, be very wary of his cane, he's really sneaky with it; tries to squash us both, says we are a nuisance," laughed both bugs.

"Two doors down is Mr. Johnson's room. He's a navy man all the way, and there are pictures of ships on practically every square inch of his walls," Festus informed Tom. Tom walked over to Mr. Johnson's doorway, and to his surprise, the man was awake and watching his television. The old navy veteran caught sight of the cat and patted the bed, motioning him to jump up and join him.

"Well, it's about time you came to meet me, Mr. Tom," he said, rubbing and scratching Tom's back. "Now I have someone else to tell my old war stories to who won't argue with me," he laughed. "You see that big contraption all decked out in the corner? That's my "ship," that's what I call it, anyhow, because it glides up and down the hallway as smooth as a clipper in calm seas," he said, as he pointed to his large motorized wheelchair.

"We'll be the best of mates" he said, as his hand made its way underneath Tom's chin. Tom, having no clue as to what ships or clippers were, or seas, for that matter, pretended to understand by laying on his back and purring up a storm as Mr. Johnson found just the right scratch spot.

"You can ride in the stern of my ship anytime you want to, Tomcat; I'm only here sometimes, whenever my family needs a break from caring for me," he said. Tom gave him a cold nose-rub good bye, jumped down from the bed, and headed for the doorway with Festus buzzing overhead.

"Mr. Johnson is the only veteran on this ward whose room I can fly into and out of as I please," remarked Festus as they headed down the hall. He guided Tom to the next stop on the tour and landed on the name plate outside the room. "Mr. Randolf is in this room, Tom; he's a former marine and mean as a snake. He has a disease called Alzheimer's. It affects the brain in a more serious way than dementia; before his time is up he'll even forget how to eat. Sad isn't it."

Up onto the bed the cat hopped, to see for himself this supposedly mean old man. Straight up to his face he went, and he kissed him directly on the nose. Mr. Randolf opened his eyes to see a large, hairy orange creature in his face, nose to nose. Tom sat his rump down on the old man's emaciated chest, and the two had a staring contest that went on seemingly forever. Mr. Randolf, gaining control of his senses at last, began to yell at the top of his lungs. "What the devil—get off of me, you hairy little beast, be gone with you, I say!" It frightened Tom so badly that he jumped off the bed and leapt to the doorway with one bound.

"We told you so," said Festus, with Tizzy chiming in.

"That's enough for me right now, kiddos; I'd better get back to the nurses' station and see what's cooking," he said still shaken from the ordeal. He ran down the waxed hallway so fast that he slid on his behind right past the station, causing an uproar of laughter. "Tom, you are going to give this ward what it has been lacking for a long time: laughter," said Festus, and Tizzy nodded in total agreement.

CHAPTER SIX:

The Field Trip

Tom settled into his new home quite easily. As the days and months went by he became an important member of the staff. Everyone adored him, except, of course, for Mr. Randolf, who continued to fuss at him at every opportunity, most of the time at the height of his vocal register. On Tuesdays he was treated to chicken, but his favorite day was Friday, which was fish day, because several patients left out tiny morsels just for him, which he collected as he did his rounds. Festus made sure he came along to get his share of what he considered a smorgasbord (by a fly's definition).

"Tom come here; I'll give you a lift," shouted Mr. Johnson, from the far end of the hallway. Mr. Johnson was one of Tom's favorite humans on the ward, and Tom ran swiftly to the motorized wheelchair, which Mr. Johnson called his "ship," and jumped on board. Mr. Johnson had fixed a special place for Tom to sit so he could see all of the goings on.

They began their rounds with their usual trip into the pastor's office so that Mr. Johnson could pocket some of the Hershey Kisses that the pastor kept in a dish on his desk; then back to the nurses' station so he could chat with Ethel, whom Mr. Johnson was kind of sweet on, then to the dayroom to pass the time with other veterans, exchanging war stories.

Their routine was the same each day, and it included passing Mr. Deacon in the hall, who waved his cane every which way, hoping to hit something, and talking to himself.

"Watch this, Tom," said Mr. Johnson, as he blew his horn right behind Mr. Deacon. "Gol darn you navy men, you're all the same; got no brains under those little white hats," yelled Mr. Deacon, as the pair moved around him and shot right past. "Trying to give me an early heart attack, are you? I'll get you for that, you swabbie," he said angrily, as he managed to hit the "ship" with his cane. "Sea water for blood, he has" he said, clutching his frail chest. Tom felt so bad for Mr. Deacon that he jumped "ship" and ran back to him and wrapped himself around one of his legs to calm him down.

"You're a good cat, Morris; too bad you've taken up with the likes of a navy man," Mr. Deacon commented, momentarily forgetting Tom's name. The two men looked at each other and began to laugh, and parted ways as they always did—each to his own room; and war had been averted for another day.

Festus, coming from out of nowhere, landed on Tom's head, buzzing more than usual. "Guess where I've been this fine day?" he asked.

"I haven't the faintest idea," said Tom.

"I made it to the second floor again today, when Domingo kept the elevator door open for a bunch of interns to get off and I flew right in, Festus said.

"He had to go to the second floor for some linens, and to make a date with the new CNA on that floor," he added. "I got to talk some more with Bird and his friends; you remember, I told you about Bird and how he helps the patients on that floor who have depression issues."

"You never told me any such thing, Festus; I'm beginning to think that you have been on this ward too long," chuckled Tom.

"Forget you, I'm telling you now. Bird said that if you ever make it to his floor, he'll let you in on the purpose for which you're really here. Bird knows a lot of stuff," he said huffily.

Tizzy, overhearing this conversation, lit on the overhead light fixture to put in her two- cents-worth of advice. "Don't listen to him, Tom; you are a cat, and, well, Bird is a bird. If they catch you two together they might think that you want to eat him or something. It wouldn't be a pleasant experience for you," she yelled back as she flew to the next light.

"We'll see about all that later, but right now I am going to take a nap, maybe on Mr. Randolph's bed," replied Tom, as he headed in that direction. "I'll just lay at his feet for awhile; that way I won't disturb him," he said to himself.

Tom had been privy to a talk between Katie and Maude a few days earlier, as they discussed Mr. Randolfs' condition. They seemed to feel that his mental problems were growing worse.

"Maybe if I sleep with him more often he won't think about anything else except the Marines," surmised Tom, as he curled up beside of the old man's feet.

"Rise and shine," shouted somebody in the hallway. Tom was brought out of a wonderful dream, where he was chasing butterflies in a huge field of yellow daffodils, the wind blowing gently and the sunshine feeling so good on his face. "Oh, my goodness, what a fantastic dream," he thought, as he roused himself from his slumber.

One look at Mr. Randolf and Tom could tell that he hadn't moved a muscle. Tom made his way to the door and stretched his back muscles, raising his butt into the air. "Another day, same routine—or maybe I'll do something different today," he purred under his breath.

"Good morning, Tom, it's going to be a great day," said Doc as he passed by.

"Meow," Tom responded, as he sat back down on his haunches for a moment. As Tom tried to formulate a new and adventurous plan for the day, he caught sight of Domingo, with his rolling laundry basket, stopping at each room to exchange linens.

"I know that Domingo will be going to the second floor today, and if I could hide in the laundry basket, then I could meet Bird; *that* would be an adventure, no boring same-old, same-old routine for me today," he thought, as he devised the daring plan in his head.

Domingo, temporarily distracted by a cute female intern who'd just walked by him, gave him the chance to make his move. So very catlike, he sauntered up to the basket and ever-so-silently tucked himself inside the bottom shelf, careful that the overlapping linens hid him.

"Good morning, Ethel," said Domingo, with his melodious Jamaican accent.

"Good morning to you, Domingo, and by the way, have you seen Tom this morning by any chance; I have his breakfast ready and it's not like him to miss a meal."

"Na, haven't seen the mon this morning; maybe he be in the dayroom," he replied.

They were now in front of the elevator, and Tom sneaked a peek at the sign that read "Be Aware of Cat."

"If I get caught, I am going to be in a *bunch* of trouble, but what the heck—live dangerously is my motto," he chuckled to himself.

The elevator door opened onto the second floor, and what seemed like a herd of people charged out. Of course, Domingo had to wait until they were all gone, but finally Tom heard the "clang" sound, and he let out a sigh of relief.

The doors opened and Domingo pushed his cart to the first room on his list. The instant Domingo entered the room, Tom ran for cover, making it to the row of green plastic chairs lined against the wall for guests. "Where in the world do I go now," he thought. "I have no clue as to where they would keep a cage full of birds," he muttered under his breath. Right on cue, he heard the sounds of birds chirping, and followed them until he came to the visitors' lounge.

Lo and behold, before his very eyes was the biggest cage he had ever seen, so shiny and gold that the reflection from sunlight bouncing off of it almost blinded him. A treasure trove of multicolored birds of every size and color were there in one spot—a cat's jackpot! Tom approached the cage with caution, so as not to frighten the birds. "Excuse me, but could you fine feathered folks tell me where to find Bird?" he asked. All beady eyes turned on him and the chirping ceased all at once as the flock of songbirds realized that there was a real, live cat sitting in front of them, and talking to boot! The sea of birds parted just like a curtain, and smack-dab in the middle was a larger-than-life, red-headed, blue-and-gold-bodied bird with a huge beak, swinging on a little wooden swing.

"I am the one you seek, Tom; I am Bird, an exotic parrot, to be precise, at your service," croaked Bird, in a baritone voice.

"I've been expecting you, cat," he said. "Festus has told me all about you and your adventures, and how you found yourself to be here at this hospital," he said, as he adjusted his sharp talons on the wooden swing. For a minute, Tom sat dumbfounded. It was completely quiet; all the other birds had remained silent in order to follow the conversation.

"To say the least, Mr. Bird, I am *shocked* at myself for being here, and of course having a feline brain, *doubly shocked* by not having the urge to eat you," replied Tom, unaware that he was licking his lips.

"But my dear fellow, we are much more civilized than that," Bird remarked in a matter-of-fact tone. "Our purpose here is to show love and compassion, to be companions to our human counterparts, our veterans; to give them a small reason to hope and also feel normal again; to be part of the real world, even if it's just for a short while." Bird, with the wisdom of age behind his words said, "As you well know, Tom, on your ward there are many critically ill patents, some at the end of their journeys.

"Festus has told me that you can inform me of my real purpose here. I'm not too sure, though, what it is I can accomplish, being just a cat and all," he said, feeling humble and totally dependent on Bird's wisdom.

"All things on earth God gave a purpose to, just like the honeybees who make the sweet honey, and the mighty trees that supply us with shade and warmth; each living thing has a reason to be here," replied Bird. "You, my dear alley cat, fit right into God's plan for the Palliative Care Unit. Your part in our veterans' final journey home is simple: to give them peace, and the acknowledgement that they do matter, because, sadly, most of these veterans have nobody in the world to love them and care for them, and sometimes they are forgotten here. You are my newly found friend, the 'Angel Cat'; the Lord told me so in a dream," said the bird solemnly.

"That's a really big responsibility. I don't know if I can live up to that job," said Tom, sitting back down in a state of shock.

"But you can, and you must, Mr. Tom, because the Lord has chosen you to be a living spirit guide, one who comforts and helps escort the soul as it leaves its earthly body on its journey to heaven," replied Bird.

Tom sat in silence for a few minutes, trying to absorb all of the things he had heard, his thoughts all a-jumble.

"Now you know your mission in life, and now you must also make it back to your ward before anyone finds you here, or we're all going to be in big trouble," commanded the big bird.

"Yes, I'll go now before they miss me, and thank you, Bird. Maybe someday we will meet again," answered Tom, as he slowly crept backwards toward the doorway.

CHAPTER SEVEN:

Mistaken Freedom

"I must find Domingo's basket!" he thought. "There it is, right in front of the elevator," he said to himself, as he made one long, running leap and burrowed back underneath the linens. "I hear Domingo coming; I guess he's made all his rounds to visit with the ladies on this floor," he laughed to himself. Domingo, waving goodbye to the staff, pushed the up-button. The doors opened right away, and he pushed in his overloaded laundry basket, cat included, right next to a very attractive young nurse. Because it was in his nature to flirt, and because he couldn't resist doing so, he totally forgot to push the button for the third floor, and, instead, they all headed down to the main floor. When they reached their destination, Domingo, as gentlemanly as he always was, pushed out his cart so that the young nurse could exit more easily. Following her around the corner in the hope of obtaining her phone number, he left the cart unattended. Thinking that because he had heard the bell ding and the cart wasn't moving anymore, that he had arrived on the third floor, Tom jumped out; not recognizing the ward, he panicked. Instead of turning left, where Domingo and the young nurse stood chatting, he turned right, and began to run, dodging in and out of throngs of humans, and found himself in the middle of the main floor of the hospital.

Seeing so much humanity at one time spooked him, and in the midst of all the screeches and screams that "There's a cat in here, a real live cat," he ran even faster.

Floyd, a maintenance worker who cleaned the floors each day, was riding his monstrous floor machine; he heard all the ruckus and saw Tom, tail tucked between his legs, running for his life. "I'll get him," shouted Floyd.

Tom, looking behind him and seeing the horrible monster-machine hot on his trail, headed straight for daylight. The front doors just happened to be open at the right time, and straight through the middle of the valet's legs he went; across the handicapped- parking lot he ran, dodging cars and humans in his quest to lose the huge machine.

"I must not stop until I reach those fishing ponds I've seen whenever I look out the pastor's window," he thought even as he panicked. Up the winding road, to the sound of tires screeching as cars stopped to avoid hitting him, on he ran. At last he reached the first pond, and crawled under a bush to rest and catch his breath.

The smell of fresh air and the feel of soft grass beneath his belly reminded him of days long past. The sunshine, the cool breeze, birds singing high up in the trees, flowers in bloom, their fragrance drifting toward him, fascinated him, and made him recall his nature as an outdoor cat—his so-called freedom. "Even though this hospital-home came about by accident, kind of, I will surely miss all of the friends that I have made on the inside," he acknowledged to himself.

Exhausted, he fell asleep, his tummy rumbling with hunger. "This had to happen on fish-day," was his last thought.

"Where's Tom; Katie, Ethel, have you two seen him at all today?" asked Maude. "No, we haven't," both answered at the same time.

"I have called for him, and looked in all the rooms," said Katie.

"So have I, and none of the veterans have seen him either. They're very upset, even Mr. Randolf," said Ethel.

"You don't suppose he found the elevator and ran off, do you?" Maude asked the nurses. The two women shrugged their shoulders in bewilderment as to Tom's whereabouts. "There's Domingo getting off of the elevator now; go down there, Katie, and check with him to find out if he's seen him," ordered Maude, a touch of fear in her voice.

Katie ran down the hall, shouting for Domingo to wait for her. "Have you seen Tom today? We can't find him anywhere on the ward."

"Na mon, I haven't. I would have seen him if he got on the elevator with me fine self," he replied.

Maude, finally hustling to the end of the hallway, gave instructions for all to search again, from top to bottom, for that darned cat.

"We have to do the very best we can before we bring this problem to the pastor's attention," she said.

Throughout the day they searched for Tom; even Mr. Johnson drove his "ship" up and down the hall, hollering for Tom to come out from his hiding place. As everyone gathered at the nurses' station during a lull in the ward's routine, their hearts were heavy because each person, in his or her own way, had become attached to the stray alley cat.

"Apparently, Tom has made it off the ward somehow, and we are going to have to inform the pastor of this situation first thing in the morning," announced Maude.

"He's going to be extremely upset; he really loves that cat," said Katie, bursting into tears. The whole group agreed that they all cared about the cat, and truly didn't want Pastor Green to be upset. Katie and Ethel ran to the bathroom to wash the tears from their faces. Jacob and Domingo, being "manly" men who didn't want to show any emotion in front of the women, went their separate ways, both lost in their private thoughts. Maude, ever the stoic one, just cussed under her breath.

Later that day, Katie and Ethel had a conversation. "Someone has to tell the patients; Mr. Deacon and Mr. Randolf are so upset they won't eat their suppers," said Ethel.

"I know; Mr. Randolf cussed me out when I entered his room a little while ago, because, according to him, 'that darn cat hadn't been around to bother him today,'" added Katie.

Pastor Green and Doc Williams entered the pastor's office the next morning to have their first cup of coffee before the workday began and they needed to make rounds. They were interrupted by all the day staff and some of the veterans, each one trying to out-talk the others. The office filled to its capacity and more.

"Everyone, please calm down now, and just *one* of you tell me what's going on here," said the pastor, as he was encircled by hysterical beings.

"I'll tell you exactly what's going on here, some nincompoop has lost Tom," piped up Mr. Johnson, as he drove the "ship" to the front of the crowded room.

"It's true, Pastor Green, and we are sorry to have to tell you this, but Tom has been missing since yesterday; he's nowhere on this floor, and we think he must have gotten onto the elevator, probably while visitors were leaving," said Maude.

Jacob entered the room at the end of that statement, and announced, "I know where Tom went; it's all over the main floor of the hospital—people couldn't stop talking this morning about how Floyd chased a cat out of the front doors yesterday."

"Apparently, nobody connected our Tom to the incident yesterday, because not a soul has spoken to me about it," remarked Doc.

"Nor to me," said the pastor. Doc Williams, hearing the emotion in the pastor's voice, ordered everyone out of the office and told them to return to their duties or to their rooms. As the last of the patients left the office, Doc turned to the pastor, who had left his desk and was staring out of his window.

"You do realize that he may never come back, don't you?" he asked.

"He'll be back; I feel it in my soul, but it's in God's hands now," Pastor Green sadly answered, and the two men stood side by side, praying for that very miracle.

CHAPTER EIGHT:

Life on the Lam

"Tizzy, stop your fluttering for a minute—Tom has escaped; he's on the outside now," stuttered Festus, trying to talk and fly at the same time.

"I heard all about it from my cousin on the main floor. Tom hid underneath Domingo's cart and he never knew it, then he got out on the wrong floor and was chased by Floyd on his Zamboni machine straight out the front door," said Festus.

"No kidding? I hope he can make it in the outside world again," replied Tizzy, as she buzzed to the next light.

Tom's stomach woke him, he was so hungry. In his dream, Katie was tossing big chunks of chicken and fish at him to catch in his mouth, as he lay like an emperor, reclining on his warm, plush cat bed. Wide awake now, he realized that he *wasn't* being fed and the ground didn't feel nearly as soft as his bed. "I must find something to eat or my stomach is going to turn inside out, for sure. I'll circle the pond and maybe I'll find some leftover scraps from last week's veterans' cookout," he thought to himself.

"Psst, psst, hey, you cat down there," called a voice out of nowhere. Tom looked around to see if he could locate the source of the voice. As he looked up, he was hit smack-dab in the middle of his forehead with a nut.

"Just had to get your attention, cat, I'm up here in the oak tree," said the voice.

Tom shook his head to clear his vision, and rubbed a paw over the forming knot on his head. He gingerly ventured another look-see upwards, and spied a fat gray squirrel, wearing some kind of brown leather cap that strapped underneath his chin, sitting on a limb, cracking a nut.

"Name is Elroy, what's your's?" he asked.

"They call me Tom, nice to meet you, um, I think," he answered, as he rubbed his knot.

"Hungry are you?" asked Elroy.

"Yes, starved," replied Tom.

"Have a couple of my nuts, then—don't worry, I won't aim for your head this time. I don't trust cats much per se, or I'd bring them down to you myself," said the squirrel.

"I won't hurt you; I like all God's creatures; we're kind of in the same boat anyway, so we should look out for each other," said Tom.

"Imagine that, a cat with a philosophical nature, don't that beat all," replied Elroy, as he posed like the famous statue of the Thinking Man. Elroy scrambled down the tree, jaws full of nuts, which he dropped at Tom's feet. "I suppose you want me to crack them for you, too, ol' wise one," he snickered.

Tom, ignoring the obvious sarcasm, pushed the nuts toward Elroy. "Yes, please, you're so much more adept at that sort of thing than I am. And, by the way, I'm a bit curious: Isn't it sort of unusual for a squirrel to be wearing a leather cap?"

"For your information, I am a direct descendent in a long line of air force squirrels, and this is an official fighter pilot's cap, handed down to me by my grandfather, the infamous "Brown Bomber," who was an ace in World War II," answered Elroy proudly.

"And where do you come from, cat, are you service-connected?" asked the squirrel. Tom told him that he wasn't, and began to tell Elroy about all of his adventures, and how he came to be here at the hospital.

"Good heavens, that's quite a tale, but what are you going to do now?" Elroy asked.

"I really don't have any good ideas about that right now; I'll just try to survive, I guess," answered Tom, chewing a mouthful of nuts.

"I'll tell you what—as soon as you finish eating, we'll go and ask Bubba what he thinks you should do," said Elroy.

"Who's Bubba?" asked Tom.

"Boy, don't you know anything? Bubba is the Kingfish and Wise One of the ponds. He knows everything about these grounds, and he'll help you for sure," replied Elroy, as he straightened his cap with his little paws.

When Tom had finished his unusual meal, together they circled the first pond while Elroy called into the water several times for the Kingfish. "No luck here; let's try the middle pond. Each pond has a small canal connecting it with the others, so he could be in any of the three," said Elroy. "Sir Bubba, where are you? Come up, please. I have a friend with me who needs your advice," he shouted.

A gigantic splash of water that covered both parties from head to toe preceded the emergence of Bubba, head just above the surface, bobbing up and down. "What do you want, Elroy; I'm busy—and who is that stranger with you? I didn't know that you associated with unfamiliar cats," he said.

"This is my new best friend, Tom, and he needs your advice on what to do, now that he's sort of a lost cat again," he answered.

Bubba swam closer to the bank, the sun glistening off his brilliant scales almost blinding Tom. Of course, being the biggest and oldest of the goldfish in all the three ponds, Bubba was the head honcho in his watery world.

"So, Mr. Tom, you find yourself in quite a dilemma do you; can't decide whether to stay or to go, is that it?" asked the goldfish.

"I'm not sure what to do," answered Tom. "What would you advise?"

"This is my advice to you today. The veterans are having their annual fishing event tomorrow.

I'll get all of the gossip from my fellow fish-friends; the veterans always release them before they leave. I will converse with them in the afternoon. Come back late tomorrow evening with Elroy, and I'll give you my advice then. Elroy, in the meanwhile, you must take him to Sassy, so that she can provide him with food and shelter, and keep him safe." And, with that, he again disappeared beneath the water.

"You'll like Sassy, she's a fancy cat, Himalayan or something like that," Elroy said to Tom.

Off they went to find the elusive feline Sassy. "Sometimes she's in the garden behind the hospital; there's always lots of good eats there," said Elroy, as he hopped along in front of Tom, chirping in his strange squirrel tongue. He showed Tom where the blackberry bushes were located as they made their way, and they grabbed a few berries to stave off the hunger pains. Elroy ran up and down several trees in order to have a better vantage point overlooking the grounds, in hopes of catching sight of the crafty kitty Sassy.

Tom, in the meanwhile, had to stop and scratch behind his ear. "Darned fleas, what a nuisance they are," he thought to himself. Suddenly, from out of nowhere, he found himself pounced on from behind and bowled over, landing at the foot of a tree. When his vision cleared, he found himself looking into the most beautiful blue eyes he had ever seen.

"Don't kill him, Sassy, he's a friend of mine," shouted Elroy, as he scrambled down from another nearby tree. "Sorry ol' man, I couldn't warn you fast enough; she's so quick and sneaky," he told Tom. "Let me introduce you two: Tom, this is Sassy, and Your Queenship, this is Tom; he's on the lam, so to speak," announced Elroy.

Sassy, still standing over Tom, relaxed and backed away from him and sat down. "Huh, not much of an alley cat, are you, if you let me sneak up on you like that," she stated flatly.

Tom, embarrassed, got up, stretching on all fours, swishing his tail, and trying to pump out his chest to look tougher and more manly.

He hissed, "I am a *very good* alley cat, smart and strong—you just got lucky, sister, that's all," he grumbled. "I was distracted by all these darned yard fleas," he added.

"Yeah, right," replied Sassy, with a hint of disdain in her voice. Both cats faced off, sizing each other up. Elroy rolled on the grass in a fit of laughter at the sight. The tension incited by Sassy's insult to Tom's manhood grew, and the cats began to circle each other, backs hunched high in the air, tails bristling. The hissing grew louder as each combatant tried to force the other to cry "uncle" first. Finally, Tom gave in, and not wanting to fight a lady anyhow, just sat back down. "I give up. I'm too tired and hungry to fight, so you win," he said.

Sassy, dumbfounded by Tom's humility, stopped her pacing and retracted her very sharp claws. "Well, I guess if you're Elroy's friend you can be mine, as well," she said.

Not wanting to stare at her too long because it might set her off again, Tom cast his eyes down as he marveled at her fluffy coat and gorgeous markings. "What a fine cat; indeed, a real lady," he thought to himself.

"Come on guys, since you're so hungry, I'll show you the best place to eat around here," said Sassy. "I was a house cat at one time, myself, until my owner moved away and couldn't take me with him, so I *still* only eat the best," she commented as they made their way across the large front lawn. "It's suppertime at the canteen," she said, as they reached their destination. The threesome made their rounds among the picnic tables filled with people eating outside in the afternoon sunshine.

Elroy, joining in, was grabbing the pieces of bread thrown his way. Sassy was right; the pieces of meat thrown their way were first-class. Finally, with their bellies full, they all stretched out under a nearby shade tree. "I'll take it from here, Elroy. I can bed Tom down at my place," Sassy said as she cleaned the last of the juices from her long whiskers. "We will see you tomorrow," they both told Elroy, as they started off on their way back to Sassy's place.

Sassy's hidden sleeping place was inside the shed at the veterans' flower and vegetable garden.

"You'll be comfortable here, Tom, there's plenty of hay and mulch to make you a real soft bed, and this place keeps you out of the weather, too," said Sassy.

The two cats settled down for the night, and both agreed to tell the other their life stories. Though Tom was exhausted from his day's adventures, long into the night they exchanged their lives' tales, some happy, others sad. Minutes before daybreak, their eyes burning with the need to sleep, they nodded off, side by side, as if they had known each other for all time.

"Rise and shine, sleepyheads," shouted Elroy from the nearest oak tree. "It's nearly noon, and you, my fine fellow, have a meeting with Bubba this afternoon." Both cats yawned, sat up, and started to groom each other. "*That didn't take long; Miss Sassy is quite the cat's meow, as far as cats go, that is,*" chuckled Elroy.

And Tom looked into those big blue eyes and felt his heart beat a bit faster.

"Come on, kids, enough of that moony stuff, you two must be hungry. We can check out the berry bush along the way to see Bubba" Elroy said.

"Good idea, little fellow, you lead the way," said Tom. Totally entranced by the swaying of Sassy's hindquarters as he walked behind her, he didn't see the groundhog hole until it was too late. "My, my, I think the boy's in love, yes siree," laughed Elroy, as he watched Tom, still starry-eyed, extricate himself from the hole.

The threesome wandered to the berry bush, where they lingered for a while, enjoying the fruit and getting a trifle messy after a game of berry pounce. When they had nibbled their fill, they continued on their way to the main road.

"We must be careful; these humans in their cars like to run down cats or any other wildlife that gets in their way," Sassy reminded the others. The traffic was truly heavy, and Tom decided to depend on Sassy's expertise as to when it was safe to cross. A car carrying five older women actually stopped for them as they hesitated near the curb, and they made it safely across. They headed for the pond to find Bubba, passing the last of the stragglers from the fishing event. When they reached the pond, scraps of leftover food littered the ground.

"This is great, Tom, we don't have to visit the canteen today; we have plenty to eat right here," said Sassy, as she started to enjoy her meal.

"Bubba, are you here?" yelled Elroy.

"Yes I am," replied the giant fish, as he emerged from underneath the fishing dock.

"I brought Tom back like you told me to, and Sassy's here, as well," said Elroy.

"Indeed you did, and hello, Miss Sassy, it's always a pleasure to see you," he said, his bulging fish eyes surveying the pair of cats. "You two seem to be fast friends already, and that is good news for sure," he commented.

Then, directing his attention toward Tom, he told him, "I have sought and gathered the information that you need from my fellow-aquatics, and it seems, Tom, that all the folks on your ward have been frantically looking for you, and are seriously upset and saddened by your departure. To leave this place, Tom, would be a grave mistake, because it is my gut feeling that you are going to play a big role in someone's life, and you will make that difference in the near future, so you must not leave these grounds, and this is my advice to you," spoke the King Fish. Then he disappeared beneath the surface, leaving only a trail of bubbles behind.

"Well, it looks like the Wise One has spoken; you are needed here for some reason yet to be discovered," chirped Elroy.

"May I stay with you, Miss Sassy? I won't be any trouble, I'm a good mouser, and I'll defend you to the death, if need be," he asked, looking sheepishly down at his paws.

Sassy, already quite content to have Tom around, as he was such a gentle cat, and a very handsome male, which didn't hurt matters either, answered him. "That's the end of this discussion. You most certainly may stay with me as long as you like, and we will have great adventures together; and besides, it gets lonely out here sometimes. I could use the company," she declared. And adventures they did have, one of which was the capture of the most notorious dog pack in the whole valley.

Word had spread all around the grounds via Elroy's cousins from the nearby woods, that the dreaded pack of canines, known as the Loners' Gang, had set up shop there and had declared the woods their exclusive turf. According to Elroy's information, the pack of dogs was planning a raid during the veterans' Fourth of July picnic. Chico, Elroy's baby cousin, claimed to have overheard the dastardly plan. "The gang plans to disrupt the picnic and steal all the food they can, even if they have to hurt humans or animals in the process," Chico told everyone at the meeting Tom had called.

"We don't have much time because the picnic is later this afternoon. We must agree on the plan of action now," Tom told the crowd of grounds-animals gathered around him. "Elroy, you get your cousins to man the trees and keep an eye out for the gang," instructed Tom.

"I'm pretty sure that today is the pound truck's scheduled run of the hospital grounds," added Sassy.

"Then leave it all to me and Sassy, we'll be the rabbits in front of the greyhound; we'll lead the pound truck right to the place of attack.

"Well, Tomcat, you seem to have everything under control and you've proven yourself to be a true leader of the grounds. I am very proud of you," Bubba said, as everyone turned to look in his direction. "But you did forget one thing: You must have an advance-warning system to alert you when the pack enters the grounds.

That's where you come in, Elroy. You and your cousins must signal Tom and Sassy the minute you spot the pack touch our soil," the fish declared.

Everyone agreed that this was a perfect plan. After all, the King Fish had given his blessing, and this was their home, and the veterans and the staff of the hospital were their family, too.

It was turning into a beautiful day, hot and sunny. White, wispy clouds rolled gently by in the blue sky. People from far and near had gathered to play games and eat hamburgers and hot dogs, and small children laughed as they chased some of Elroy's kin 'round and 'round the trees. Everyone was waiting to celebrate Independence Day.

The festivities had not been going on for very long when some of Elroy's cousins reported to him that the dog pack was getting ready to race out of the woods. Fortunately, preparations had progressed. Mr. Groundhog had already dug a bunch of large holes, just in case Tom's plan didn't work. Tom and Sassy were stationed at the front gate, on the lookout for the much-hated pound truck. Like clockwork, the truck turned the corner and entered through the gate, just as a relayed message of chirping squirrels reached the cats' ears, signaling the advance of the gang onto the grounds.

"It's now or never, old girl," Tom whispered to Sassy, as they both dashed out in front of the pound truck. The driver, thinking this was his lucky day, increased his speed down the narrow, curvy road so as not to lose sight of the two cats.

They ran as fast as they could towards the chirping squirrels, the pound truck in hot pursuit. Past the picnic they went, straight up the road they ran, right into the middle of the pack of dogs. So stunned were they by the sheer audacity of a pair of mangy cats invading their space, the Loners' Gang stopped dead in the road in front of the pound truck, which had come to a screeching halt. Before they could react, several cat-snatchers had jumped from the truck and began to round them all up, every single dog.

Tom and Sassy joined in with their grounds-workers friends and the veterans to celebrate a job well done and to enjoy a fine summer night of glorious fireworks.

So that's the way it went: month followed month, summer into fall. The pair of stray cats grew closer, and enjoyed many wonderful and contented days and nights together. As the days began to get shorter, the leaves turned color; fall was in the air, and the wind had a slight chill to it. All the creatures that called the grounds their home began to get ready for the upcoming winter weather. The squirrels gathered more nuts, the groundhog dug deeper holes, and the birds began their journey southward.

One evening, after supper at the canteen, as the two cats groomed each other, Sassy made a comment that took Tom by surprise. "It won't be long before we have more mouths to feed—do you understand what that means, Tom?" she asked. Not ready to give up any extra food by answering her verbally, Tom simply shook his head. "Not yet, you silly alley cat, but there will be, and not too far off into the future, if I've figured correctly," giggled Sassy.

Tom sat up straight, ears all cocked back, a perplexed look on his handsome face. Then it hit him, smack-dab in the center of his obtuse male brain. "You mean...?" He could hardly get out the words. "Yes, that is exactly what I mean," Sassy replied, as she rolled onto her back and playfully batted at him with her paws. "You, my dear Tom, are going to be a papa cat, and pretty soon, too," she laughed.

"I am gonna be a father, a real father, a bona fide family cat," he exclaimed at the top of his lungs as he ran in circles around Sassy. "I've got to spread the news—I must tell Elroy and Bubba, and, oh, if only I could tell all my friends on the ward—Festus, Tizzy, and of course, the pastor; but I can't do that unless I go back inside," he mumbled to himself. Tom still missed his friends in the hospital, but not wanting to lose his freedom, or Sassy, decided against the plan—for now, anyway—pushing it to the back of his mind. Jumping for joy, chasing his own tail in circles like a kitten, he yelled for all to hear.

"I'm going to be a family cat, did you hear me, Elroy?" he asked, as he parked himself underneath the squirrel's favorite tree.

"I think that everybody in the valley heard that announcement, Mr. Tom," answered the squirrel, as he emerged from his emergency nut stash, leather cap sideways on his small head. "I'm on my way right now, via treetop, to spread the good news, and I'll stop by the ponds to fill Bubba in on the newest development," he said. "This is a very large detour in Tom's life; I wonder how it's going to affect his destiny," thought Elroy, as he leapt from tree to tree on his mission to spread the news.

Bubba the All Knowing was patrolling the dock area looking for any leftover worms that might have fallen off hooks during the fishing event. Elroy, winded from his long and perilous trip across the main road, started shouting for the King Fish even before he reached the pond.

"You don't have to yell so loud, squirrel, I'm not deaf, even if you can't see my ears," gurgled Bubba. "I already know what you have come to tell me," he said, blowing bubbles in the water.

"How is that?"

"It's why they call me the Wise One"; I know all things that happen on these sacred grounds, just as my father and great-grandfather did before me," he replied. (Bubba had already sensed the attraction between the two cats, so it wasn't hard to figure the outcome, but he wasn't about to let Elroy in on that secret.)

"I can read your mind, squirrel. If what you really want to know is whether this joyful news will change Tom's destiny, the answer is, 'yes and no.' The Tomcat will have a serious decision to make in the future, and it's coming sooner than he knows," predicted the fish.

Tom treated Sassy as if she were a queen. Only the best scraps would do for her in her "delicate condition."

He gathered extra hay and strips of cloth he found laying around the shed to make her bed as soft as possible. Tom did all things for her as her belly began to show signs of the upcoming event. She was a bit tired and sluggish most of the time: much more a stay-at-home mother-to-be.

"It's raining outside, and it's colder than yesterday, so you just stay in bed, and I will go and fetch us something to eat," said Tom, as he poked his head out of the shed door. "How do you feel today, my little mother-to-be?" he asked.

"I feel extremely fat," replied Sassy, as she rolled onto her back, big belly protruding like a ripe watermelon ready to burst. Tom placed his paw on her tummy and felt the kick of his soon-to-be offspring. "Pretty active this morning; they must be hungry," he said. Tom gave Sassy a loving lick between her eyes, then departed their humble little home in search of something special for his lady-love to eat.

"What a nasty, dreary day this is," he thought, as he made his way to the canteen. When he reached his destination, there sat Elroy, on top of the picnic table, cracking a nut, as usual. The resident groundhog was underneath the table, catching the bits and pieces that fell through the cracks.

"Good morning, Tom," they cheerfully chorused. "If you're looking for some breakfast out here, you won't find it; it's too rainy, so all the people are eating inside today," said the groundhog.

"Well, I guess the only alternative I have is to Dumpster-dive. Sassy has been having some strange cravings lately; maybe I can find a treat in there for her this morning," said Tom.

"We'll help you look," replied Elroy and the groundhog. So all three friends climbed into the big green Dumpster in their quest for a special breakfast for the expectant mother.

"Hey, guys, I found a carrot, good for the eyes, you know" yelled Elroy, as he burrowed beneath a ton of trash.

"I managed to find a half-eaten apple," Tom yelled back.

"Boys, I've hit the jackpot, if my smeller is working right! I've found an almost-full can of tuna fish," snorted the groundhog, as he dragged the can through the hole in the side of the Dumpster.

The three friends divided up their finds, giving Tom the lion's share, and went their separate ways. Tom returned to the shed and surprised Sassy with the gourmet meal. As he lay and watched her consume the largest portion of the treats, as she always did, the strangest feeling of loss and despair washed over him. He could sense that something in his world was amiss. The sensation persisted as he watched Sassy finish her meal and meticulously groom her long, luxurious coat. It was an instinctual feeling of being needed, somehow, somewhere.

The day progressed, the rain stopped, and the pair decided to take their regular evening walk so Sassy could get her exercise. Tom still couldn't shake the strange sensation that something unusual was about to happen.

"Tom, we seem to always end up here at the ambulance doors each evening about the same time; why is that?" asked Sassy. "Tom, are you listening to me?" she asked a second time. Getting no quick response, she went to the fountain to get a drink of water, the spray dampening her fur.

Tom, sitting upright, one ear cocked towards Sassy's chatterings and the other one toward the goings-on at the Emergency Room doors, reflected on his answer to that question.

"I'm not sure, my dear, but I feel like I must be here for some reason." He sighed. "But we must go now; it's getting late, and the night air is not a healthy choice for you," he said as he moved alongside her, looking back once more before they departed. A strong sense of wanting to remain in that very spot persisted. However, he took the lead, and they single-filed their way home to their warm shed. He gazed down upon Sassy's beautiful face as she slept, and thanked God for her and his unborn kittens. Covering her up and kissing her forehead, he snuggled close and drifted off into an uneasy sleep.

The dream woke him; he could not remember any of it, but he had knots in his stomach, which made him feel shaky all over. Tom took one last look at his lady-love as she lay sleeping before he went out into the early-morning chill. "I must find Elroy," he thought.

"Elroy, it's Tom, please come down for a minute, I have a big favor to ask of you," he yelled up at the hole in the squirrel's favorite oak tree. Elroy, irritated by being interrupted midway in the pursuit of his favorite pastime of sorting and counting his winter nuts, barely stuck out his head, cap all askew.

"What the dickens do you want this early, Tom," he asked, sounding a little grouchy.

"Elroy, do you remember what Bubba told me a long time ago, when I first met him?" he asked.

"How in the world can I remember that far back? Bubba says a lot of things; after all, he is, to quote himself, the "Wise One," chuckled Elroy, landing head-first at the base of the tree, rolling to end up at Tom's feet.

"I'm being serious," said Tom, in his sternest voice.

"Okay, all right—no reason to get your fur all up on end," replied the squirrel, brushing himself off and straightening up his cap. "I seem to remember something about a hard decision or something to that effect."

"For a few days now, I have had some really strange and strong feelings about being needed for something important. The sensation is the most intense whenever I go near the ambulance area of the hospital," reflected Tom. "I can't explain what the pull is, but it is so strong that I feel that I must go there by myself tonight," he said. "The favor I need from you is to watch over Sassy for me. Just on the slightest chance something were to happen to me, can I count on you?" he asked his friend.

Elroy, hearing the serious tone in Tom's voice, knew this was for real, and not a joke. *"Of course you can, my good friend. I'll defend her with my life, if need be, but Tom, surely nothing is going to happen to you—what could happen if you just watch the ambulance entrance?" he asked, a bit confused.

"I'm not sure, maybe nothing, but something keeps drawing me back there, and I must have your promise, since Sassy is so close to having the kittens," answered Tom.

"I promise, Tom" said Elroy, with an emotional stutter in his voice.

CHAPTER NINE:

A Time for Everything

As the dawn was turning into a brand-new day, Tom returned to the shed, where Sassy was still sleeping soundly. He curled up beside her and drifted off to sleep. When they both awoke it was already late afternoon, and Sassy was starving, as most expectant mothers are for the majority of the time—she was ready to eat. They made their normal rounds, visiting all their friends, even braving the road-crossing to get to the pond in hopes of talking to Bubba about the upcoming birth. They yelled to get the fish's attention several times, but he never surfaced, so they went on their way, hitting the canteen just in time for supper. Elroy and a few of his cousins, along with the groundhog, were already there.

"Slim pickin's today," said the groundhog. "But we did manage to save you and your lady here half-a-piece of some kind of mystery meat with brown stuff on it," they all announced proudly.

"Elroy, you're very quiet this evening; what's wrong?" asked Sassy, as she enjoyed her supper.

"Nothing is wrong, just a small family matter I've been studyin' on; nothing for you to worry about," he replied, glancing over at Tom.

"That's right, you don't have to worry about a thing but getting your beauty sleep tonight," Tom said, giving Elroy the eyeball.

"Aren't we going on our usual stroll of the grounds before we retire for the evening, Mr. Tomcat?" she asked, looking perplexed.

"Not tonight, my dear kitty, you look a bit tired, and I am also weary. We should turn in early and get a full night's sleep," replied Tom, trying to sound as normal as possible. Sassy seemed to accept this explanation, and they both headed back to their home to bed down for the night. When Sassy was sound asleep, Tom tiptoed to the shed door, and looking back one last time, hoped he was doing the right thing, and that Sassy would eventually understand if he didn't ever come back home. He gently pushed open the shed door just a little, so it wouldn't squeak, then slipped through, making his way to the ambulance doors. The night air was crisp; a slight shiver went through his body as he made his bed on top of the round, stone table. His thoughts raced around in his head, thoughts of Sassy never forgiving him for leaving her. The only light in the darkness came from the exit sign above the emergency doors. As Tom began his wait, he curled himself into a ball, tail covering his face for warmth, and he drifted off into an uneasy sleep.

Somewhere in the midst of his dream of chasing Dinkles from one mouse hole to another, he was jarred awake by a loud, harsh siren.

The sound was coming from the direction of the gatehouse. Entering the property was an ambulance like the one that had taken Miss Opal away.

The ambulance driver stopped to speak with the gatekeeper, then proceeded to the Emergency Room entrance and began to back in. The doors swung open, and somewhere in the innermost region of Tom's brain, intuition sprang forth, and filled his whole being with the utmost feeling of urgency. There seemed to be a connection between him and this particular event. The feeling made Tom shiver all over, and for the first time in a long time, he felt the need to be back on his ward in the hospital. He knew that he had to act quickly or the doors would shut, and there was no other way to get in. His last coherent thought was of precious Sassy and his family-to-be, and with that last thought, he hit the ground running, making a beeline toward the open doors. Just before the doors closed, he ran in ahead of the paramedics, who were so preoccupied with their patient that they didn't see him.

Racing to the row of green plastic chairs lined against the wall just in front of the elevator without detection, he gave a long sigh of relief. The paramedics rolled in the patient, and stopped right in front of where he lay hidden. "Now what," Tom thought to himself. He noticed that the sheet that covered the patient was just long enough to hide a cat. "I'll pull the same trick I did on Domingo and hide under the rolling bed's bottom," he said under his breath.

He made a quick dash under the sheet, while the nurse and the paramedics had their backs turned, discussing what floor and room the patient was to be taken to. Tom relaxed, pleased with himself for being so clever, and hoping beyond hope that he'd make it to the correct floor.

As the nurse moved closer to the gurney, he caught some of the conversation between her and the paramedics:

"So, this gentleman's name is Kenneth Francisco, is that correct?" asked the nurse. "Yes, indeed, he's a transport from Valley Hospital," replied one of the paramedics, reading from his chart. The nurse proceeded to check the patient's vital signs and record them. A second nurse on duty had already made Mr. Francisco an identification bracelet, and she gently strapped it to his wrist. All this seemed to take hours, but it really had been only a few minutes until Tom heard the head nurse speak again.

"Okay, gentlemen, he's all clear on this end; you may take him to the third floor Palliative Care Ward, Room 313."

Tom's ears pricked up at the mention of that room; he recognized it immediately as one of those set aside for gravely ill veterans. He heard the familiar "ding" of the elevator as it stopped, and the doors opened so they could board. The two paramedics chatted about their day, and what was to come before their shift was over, as they all made their way to the third floor.

Ding, the doors opened, and Tom stole a peek from underneath the sheet, putting his nose up to sniff as he did so; everything looked and smelled the way he remembered it. He ducked back inside the gurney as the paramedics pushed it out and rolled it down the hallway. It came to an abrupt halt near the end of the hall, and he heard a familiar voice, that of the sweet Miss Katie. Then more voices he knew chimed in: there were Ethel, Domingo, and now the booming voice of Maude. "They must have stopped at the nurses' station," he guessed.

"I'll take Mr. Francisco's paperwork, if you'd please give it to me, and you men can take him right to Room 313," said Maude. The gurney started to roll again, and then it took a sharp right turn and came to a complete stop. Tom, not wanting to chance peeping out at this time, stayed put, as he heard other people entering the room.

"Nice and easy, fellows, let's get this dear gentleman into bed and make him as comfortable as possible," said Katie. Tom listened intently as the men and women transferred the veteran from the gurney to the bed. "According to his chart, it seems that he's had a series of strokes, he has diabetes, and is in the later stages of dementia," read Ethel.

"From what we've been told, he has had a really hard time of it. The last stroke left him weakened on both sides, and his range of motion is nearly non-existent. He also is unable to swallow," said the head paramedic.

Maude entered the room; Tom identified her by her heavy footsteps. "The family chose not to have a feeding tube surgically inserted because of Mr. Francisco's dementia, and no IV fluids, either," commented Maude.

"We'll hook him up to a morphine pump and make him as pain-free as possible," said Katie, as Tom listened intently to the women's conversation. The paramedics said their goodbyes and wished Mr. Francisco the best.

"This poor man is in what we call his last stages of life, and all we can do for him is keep him free of pain, and give him small comforts to make him feel less stressed and more as if he were at home," Maude said as she swabbed out his mouth with cool water. "As you know, he can still hear us, so we must be gentle in our speech and the tones we use so that we don't upset him," remarked Katie, as she ever-so-lightly sponged off his forehead. Ethel kept busy throughout this commentary, hooking up the morphine pump and the heart monitor.

Although the paramedics had left the gurney in the room, Tom knew it would soon be returned to the Emergency Room, and decided he must make his move. With one quick leap he landed under the bed without being detected. Just in time, too, because Domingo came back in to retrieve the gurney.

It felt like an eternity before Tom's friends left the room.

They finished up what they had to do, and covered their patient with a quilt that Katie said was from his grand-daughter—a piece of home, so to speak. When the room was silent at last, Tom eased himself from underneath the bed and jumped lightly upon the end of the bed to take a personal look at the man lying there.

Having overheard some details about Mr. Francisco, he knew that at one time in his life, he had been a very stocky and robust individual, slightly on the short side, and compact. But the person lying perfectly still in this bed was only a wisp of a man, nearly bald. What white hair he did have left was neatly trimmed, as was his full white mustache. "A very nice-looking man, with a gentle aspect to his face," thought Tom as he studied his features. Mr. Francisco was perfectly still, eyes closed, his prominent nose flaring with each breath, his mouth open. Tom crept slowly onto the man's chest and lay down, feeling the heartbeat beneath his own.

He moved closer to lick clean the beads of perspiration from the man's brow and felt the immediate bond between them, the old man's need for comfort and companionship, and his real need for the touch of loved ones. For a split second, it felt like the man's breathing eased, and a small sigh escaped his parched lips.

After he groomed Mr. Francisco, as he would do any dear friend, he looked at his patient and understood what Miss Opal and Bubba had been trying to tell him. He was supposed to be here at this very moment in time, and it had been God's plan all along; Tom's destiny. He would take this responsibility very seriously indeed.

And so Tom jumped down off the bed and walked over to the doorway. "I might as well get it over with; everyone is going to freak out the second they see me walking down the hallway, anyway." He peeked out the door, and because it was still early morning, there weren't many people out and about as yet. "So far, so good," he thought. "I'll stop by Tom's Place, if it's still here; there's nothing like a bit of excitement to make a kitty have to go potty," he laughed.

Now that his covert operation was over, he had no need to hide anymore, so he marched directly down the middle of the hallway, as if he'd never left the joint.

He came upon his old room first, with the sign still hanging above the door. He peered inside—no food or water, but thank goodness his litter box was still in the same spot. After doing his business and giving the room a good, generous spraying to mark his turf, he ventured back into the hall again, intent on visiting his old buddies.

"Oh my God," screamed Ethel, sprawling head first in the hall, medicine bottles and pill cups going every which way. Not expecting to trip over a cat that had been missing for so long, she was in total shock. Practically screaming it, all she could manage to get out of her mouth was, "He's back! Tom's back!" as she searched the floor for the runaway pill bottles. Tom, finding the situation amusing, just sat still in the middle of the floor to await his fate. Either they would accept him back or throw him out. He had hoped to visit Mr. Johnson, Mr. Deacon and Mr. Randolf before he'd made himself known, but he had to admit, this was a hilarious way to make his debut.

Pastor Green, hearing all of the commotion, came out of his office to see what all the fuss was about. Patients spilled out of their rooms, and the rest of the staff came running. Completely encircled by all of his adopted family, gazing at each familiar face, he did what any self-respecting cat of his stature would do in a situation like this: he yawned.

"Well, don't that beat all, gone all this time, worried the daylights out of everybody thinking he was lost or hurt, or worse—and here he sits, like a king or something, as if nothing in the world has happened," Maude cried out, absolutely flabbergasted.

"Make way I say, move out of the way or I'll run you aground," shouted Mr. Johnson, weaving his way down the corridor aboard his "ship." "Tom, is that you, for real, my little buddy?" he asked, as he parted the crowd to see for himself. "Thank goodness you came back; you have been sorely missed."

"Mr. Randolf complains each day that he doesn't have that darn cat to fuss at anymore; he says thing's are *boring* around here without you," said Mr. Johnson, as he rubbed Tom's head. "Hop on board, Tomcat, and I'll get you away from this gawking crowd. We've got lots to catch up on, yes we do, indeed," he said, patting Tom's favorite riding spot on the "ship."

"All right, let's break it up here, everybody back to your duties, breakfast trays need to be handed out, you know," said the pastor, a small smile beginning to show at the corners of his mouth.

"You go on ahead with Mr. Johnson, Tom. I'll bring your breakfast to his room," offered Jacob. With one leap, Tom landed in his favorite riding spot, remembering to brace himself, because Mr. Johnson's driving skills, or lack thereof, were the stuff of which legends were made.

Taking in this whole scenario were Festus and Tizzy, both having lit on the light fixture directly above the place in the hall where the encounter/smashup had occurred. Tizzy was in such a state of shock at seeing Tom come back from what she presumed was the dead that she lost all sense of direction, and began to circle the light fixture over and over again. "I'll find out all the juicy details for you Tizzy, while you try to compose yourself," said Festus, as he flew as fast as he could to catch up with the pair.

Mr. Johnson just had to stop off at Mr. Deacon's room to show off the new arrival. On seeing him, and not having changed a bit, he pointed his cane at him and started to rant about him running away.

Mr. Johnson had soon heard enough of his epithets, and muttered a few choice words himself to the cane-waving man. The "captain" and his "first mate" turned around and headed on down the hall. "Next stop Mr. Randolf," he said.

"Look who's here to visit with you, even though you are an old crusty marine," chuckled Mr. Johnson, as they entered the old man's room. They found it dimly lit; the curtains had yet to be pulled back to let in the daylight, and Mr. Randolf was still snoring.

"Wake up, old friend," Mr. Johnson called in a soft voice, so as not to startle the old gentleman.

"Who do you think you are, waking me up, and who are you, anyway?" asked the cantankerous marine veteran.

"And what's that hairy beast doing in my room—I hate animals, especially cats, so go away and leave me alone, and take that fish-eating rat-catcher with you," he shouted as loudly as his poor lungs would allow.

"Calm yourself down, now, we're leaving; I just thought you might remember Tom and want to say hello," said Mr. Johnson as he backed the "ship" up. Mr. Randolf raised himself slightly on his elbows and squinted at the pair of intruders. "Tom—I do remember that name from a long time ago, but my mind is all a-jumble. I'm sorry that I yelled at you and your partner, whoever you are," he said, as he stared at the two of them, frustration showing on his face. Mr. Johnson backed the "ship" out into the hallway, apologizing for Mr. Randolf's behavior and explaining to Tom that his condition was worsening every day.

Festus reached Mr. Johnson's room ahead of the pair, and lit on the lampshade so he would not miss any of the tall tales of Tom's adventures. The man and the cat entered, still aboard the "ship," and they pulled up beside the breakfast tray. "Look, Tom, they left your food in front of the sink, so hop off and chow down."

Festus, not being able to stand it any longer, flew down from the lampshade and landed on Tom's right paw to get the scoop of the year, and to steal a couple of bites of breakfast, as well. "Where have you been all this time?" he asked.

"It's a long story, Festus and we'll talk later about it, I promise, but right now I need to eat something, and then I must go back down the hall to check on Mr. Francisco," answered Tom in between bites.

"He's the new veteran who just came in, right? I overheard Maude telling Doc Williams that his family will be arriving shortly," said Festus.

"Here you go, Tom, you can have some of my scrambled eggs," Mr. Johnson said, placing some spoonfuls into Tom's bowl.

"Sorry Festus, but I'm starved, so you go ahead and check on Tizzy, make sure she's all right, and I'll meet you in a little while at my place to talk some more," he said, cleaning up the last of the warm egg.

"Great idea, old chum, Tizzy was a bit shook up to see you again," replied Festus as he headed for the door.

"To tell you the truth, Tomcat, we were all very worried about you after you left; the atmosphere was really depressing around here" he said, as he flew out the door.

Tom licked his bowl clean, and gave himself a good once-over washing with his rough, pink tongue. Out of nowhere came the strongest urge to look out of the window. He leapt upon the windowsill and focused his attention on the path to the canteen. Because this was the time of morning that the two of them used to come this way, Tom had high hopes of seeing Sassy. "I hope that she will understand, someday, why I had to leave her, and that she knows that Elroy will watch over her and my family for me," he thought to himself. He sighed sadly. But no sign could he see of Sassy anywhere, as he sat alone in the window pining for his one true soul mate.

Shaking off the feeling of sadness that he was experiencing, he knew that it was time to visit Room 313. Faintly he heard Katie calling him. "Here kitty, kitty," she called. He jumped over to where Mr. Johnson, on the bed, was struggling with his trousers, having just put both legs in the same leg hole, and gave his arm a nose-nudge to say "see you later." He then marched up the hall, dodging the human traffic along the way, past the visitors' lounge and the nurses' station, to find himself in front of Mr. Francisco's room, where he had seen Katie enter a few minutes earlier. He heard a murmur of voices, and although the door was ajar, he hesitated to go in right away, but sat down to listen.

Pastor Green and Katie were in the room, speaking to someone whose voice he didn't recognize. The hushed tones of several children drifted out to Tom's ears, their sadness and heartbreak very apparent.

The need to check on his "patient" so overwhelmed Tom that he threw caution to the winds, pushed open the door with his head, and made his way to the bed. He jumped onto the bed and found himself surrounded by a host of Mr. Francisco's family. "Let me introduce you all to our resident cat—Tom is his name. He has taken quite an interest in your loved one," said the pastor. Before Tom knew it, loving hands came from every direction to rub him on his head and back, one little girl child even scratching his favorite itch spot behind his ears.

A middle-aged woman said, "God bless you, Tom; my dad loves cats, and I know that he misses the cat companion he had to leave at home, just as she misses him.

"I truly feel in my heart that he can sense your presence, and I'm sure it will comfort him and ease his suffering to have you here," said an older lady.

Mr. Francisco moaned, and Tom moved up closer to lay upon his chest, purring softly. He knew that Mr. Francisco could still hear and feel, and he wanted him to know that he was close by and keeping watch.

"Pastor Green, let me introduce you to my family. This is my daughter, Sabrina; my grandchildren, Joshua, Kaila Marie, and Damon John; and of course, myself—I'm Sharon, and this is my husband, Charles," said the lady, whom Tom now understood to be "his patient's" daughter. "How do you do," said the pastor as he shook all of the family members' hands. "Now, Sharon, let's talk some about your dad—tell me all about him and his life," said the pastor.

So Sharon began to tell stories about her dad's life and adventures. She included the fact that his nickname was "Mr. John," given to him by her late mother, "Tiny," which was part of a private joke between the two—and the name just stuck. He came from a long line of rock masons, a large family of twelve, born and raised in the Catawba Valley. He had served his country, first in the army, and later ending his career as a staff sergeant in the air force. "My dad was the most generous of men, loved his family above all else, and never met a stranger. He was easy-going, kind, and a fun-loving person who never ran out of jokes. His eye for the ladies never left him; he was a bit of a flirt," recalled his daughter. The other family members joined in to recall their most cherished memories of Mr. John.

Tom drifted off to sleep, content to listen to the beat of his friend's heart, calmer now that he knew his family was gathered around him. When Tom awoke from his nap, the only people left in the room were Mr. John's daughter and granddaughter.

He changed his position to lay alongside Mr. John's leg so he could hear the two women's conversation.

"I really feel that we made the right decision to move Dad here to the Veterans' Hospital," said Sharon.

"Yes, I agree; I think this room emits a certain warmth and feeling of being at home," replied Sabrina. "All the staff are ready and willing to help out, and they really seem to care about John's comfort," she added.

"I can't quite get over this cat being here, and I really feel it's a blessing to Dad," remarked Sharon, as she patted her father's arm. "It's such a relief Just to be able to leave for a few minutes to take a break and not have to worry about Dad being alone, because I know that Tom will watch over him," she said.

"Mama, we all need some rest. John would be fussing at us if he could, for not taking care of ourselves," Sabrina commented as she swabbed out her grandfather's mouth with his favorite kind of soda, Orange Crush.

"You're right, as always; he'd tell us both, if he could still talk, to hop into that extra bed over there and get some shut-eye," Sharon said, as she tried to arrange her tousled black hair back into the knot on top of her head. Tom watched as Sabrina dipped a washcloth in cool water and wrung it out before she gently washed Mr. John's face and balding head.

"Give him a kiss, Sabrina, and we'll come back in a few hours, after we get some rest," said Sharon.

"I must talk to Pastor Green about saying a prayer for Dad before we leave," she remarked, bending over to touch her father's face. "Love you, Dad, we'll be back soon, and Tom is here with you; he's a big fat orange alley cat, and he kind of reminds me of Chuck, the orange tabby you and Mom had years ago. He'll protect you and keep you company until we return," she whispered into Mr. John's ear. The women each gave Tom a rub on the head before they left the room on their way to find the pastor.

Festus was waiting on the doorknob for them to leave. He flew straight in and landed on Mr. John's belly to continue his conversation with Tom.

"I figured I'd find you here, since you didn't show up at your place," he said. "Sad, isn't it. Mr. John has suffered for years from a bunch of mini-strokes, which caused his dementia; diabetes ruined his eyesight; and this last series of strokes caused him not to be able to swallow," Festus explained to Tom. "I overheard Maude and Katie talking, and they said that the family chose not to insert a feeding tube because he really enjoyed his food, especially with a glassful of ice-cold water; they felt that he wouldn't want to live a half-life, and not be able to enjoy those simple pleasures," he told Tom.

Tom, having known hunger and thirst in his short life, felt real compassion for the old gentleman he was guarding.

"I overheard his great-grandchildren talking, and according to them, he was the most generous and kind man, and he loved to tell them ghost stories, particularly one called "Bloody Bones," which they all agreed scared the dickens out of them," Tom noted.

"Yes, I bet it did; I also heard the two women talking to the pastor about Mr. John's fine sense of humor, even in the worst of circumstances," replied Festus. "Now that he's resting pretty well, why don't you fill me in on your adventures—tell me everything, and don't leave out any details!" said Festus, his many-faceted eyes bulging with excitement. Tom shifted his position so he wouldn't lean on Mr. John and cause him pain, and began to tell the story about how he came to find himself on the outside. He spoke of meeting Elroy, the squirrel that wore a fighter pilot's cap, and about the huge goldfish named Bubba that lived in the three ponds and could tell your future.

Tom left for last the meeting of Sassy and the upcoming arrival of a whole new family. He also explained his reason for coming back.

"Imagine that! You're about to become a father," mused Festus.

"Yes, I am, and any day now," replied Tom, with much pride in his voice.

"I must go and tell Tizzy; just think—more little Toms running around here. I'll also relay the information to my cousins so they can carry it on to Bird," Festus said over his shoulder, as he hurriedly flew from the room.

Tom shook his head in amusement at Festus, and gave his patient a lick on the hand, and a head-bump as well, before he jumped down to make his way to the front window of the ward, where he hoped to see some sign of Sassy mooching around the grounds. He sat there for some minutes, just looking out the window. Because it was Sunday, and the regular crowd of people were still in church, the grounds were all but deserted. The only human he saw was Mr. John's daughter, sitting alone on a bench surrounded by a few oak trees, one lone squirrel above her head enjoying his nuts. "Must be one of Elroy's kin," he thought. "I guess I'll make my rounds of the veterans who don't go to church," and he jumped down from the windowsill.

He went to each room, one after the other. Mr. Randolf was asleep, of course, and Mr. Johnson was washing up in his bathroom, his "ship" completely blocking the doorway. Tom had passed Mr. Deacon in the hallway earlier; he'd had to cross to the opposite side to avoid his wandering cane and possible loss of life from it. He finally made his way back to Room 313 and peered in.

Maude and Ethel, along with Jacob, were changing Mr. John's pajamas and bedclothes, all three of them doing all the special things that nurses do for their patients. Because Tom felt he would only be in their way if he attempted to join "his" patient at that moment, he decided to visit with Pastor Green for awhile; he was sure that one of the other pastors was performing the church services that day.

And there he was, sitting at his beaten-up old desk.

The pastor was writing something, and he seemed to be stuck on just what he wanted to say, because he was nibbling on his pen and had a far-away look in his eyes. His gaze shifted to Tom sitting in his doorway. "Come in here, fellow; we need to have a talk," he told Tom.

Tom jumped up on the desk, scattering all the papers again as he did so. "Truly, Tomcat, I have missed you and I'm so thankful that you came back to us—you have brought the spirit back to this ward," said the pastor. "You can't possibly understand, being just a cat, but somehow God placed you here with us for just that purpose," and he tickled Tom's belly. "Tom, I'm going to ask you for your help. Mr. John's daughter wants me to say a prayer for her dad today. He's lived a good, honest life, and being a God-fearing woman, she wants me to ask for God's forgiveness for any wrongs he has done in his life; as you well know, none of the Lord's creatures are perfect," he said matter-of-factly. "I also want to read this scripture, Ecclesiastes 3:1, out loud, and if it sounds about right to you, give me some kind of sign, okay?" he asked.

Tom listened carefully as the pastor read the passage that began with "There is a time for all things..." and all the nice words he had written down about Mr. John. He showed his approval by meowing loudly and rubbing himself along the pastor's arm, then planting a big wet kiss on his nose. "I'm glad you agree with me, Tom, and, by the way, I have been noticing you looking out all of the windows. I hope you don't want to leave us again so soon," he said, as he gathered up his papers and left the room.

Tom sat there for a few minutes, wondering if the pastor would understand about Sassy and his new family; knowing the kind of person he was, Tom felt he would.

Evening had descended on the ward, and after eating his supper and making his usual rounds, Tom found his way back to Room 313, which was again filled with family. Mr. John's daughter was holding his hand as Pastor Green began his prayer. Tom hopped onto the extra bed and listened intently to what the pastor said. After the prayer and the blessing were over, it was very quiet; the only sound that could be heard was the sniffling of the children. Tears lined the faces of all in the room, and Tom knew that the man in the bed was greatly loved by all. Even Maude, having witnessed great loss and sadness in her professional career as a nurse, wiped a tear from her eye. The family thanked the pastor, and all of them left except for Sharon, Sabrina and Kaila Marie.

Tom, sensing the raw emotion in the room, moved over to Mr. John's bed in order to comfort him and his family. "We love you, Dad" Sharon said, as she took his hand and placed it upon Tom's back. "Dad, we have to leave for a few minutes, but Tom is here with you, so you won't be alone," she said. Tom looked at Mr. John's face, and knew it wouldn't be long now, because he had seen that peaceful expression once before, on baby kitten's face. He heard

Domingo call him to give him his evening bowl of milk, but Tom didn't stir; he didn't want to leave his friend's side. Katie entered the room to check on her patient's breathing, and because Mr. John's panting had slowed, she decided to give him oxygen to ease his labored breathing.

Tom dozed off to sleep and dreamed of Sassy giving birth. Kitten after kitten kept coming from her until there was an army of hungry babies yowling to be fed. He woke up in a cold sweat: "Thank you, Lord; it was only a dream," he whispered to himself.

"Ganny, Tom looks like he's seen a ghost," Kaila said, as she entered her great- grandfathers' room ahead of the other two women.

"He does look like he's had a fright, but didn't I tell you he would still be here?" Sharon said to her granddaughter.

"Let's take turns talking now, so John'll know we're with him, and that we'll take care of him, and that we love him."

"Tom, you are *just* what we all needed—you make this place feel like home to us," Sabrina said, off-subject but sincere, as she stroked his shiny tail.

"Dad, I know you can hear me, and I want you to know that you are not in a nursing home; I didn't break my promise to you," Sharon said. "You are in a very nice room in the VA Hospital, with your very own quilt that Sabrina brought from home to keep you warm," she finished.

"Mom, I'm so glad this place was available to John. I know from talking with him on many occasions how much he feared going to a nursing home," commented Sabrina, as she tenderly covered up her grandfather.

"John, it's Kaila. I want you to know that you don't have to worry about us kids. We remember all the things you've taught us, and you will alway's be with us in our hearts, and we'll be all right," she said, lifting his hand to touch her face. Tom lay quietly and watched this close-knit family who obviously loved each other very much, comfort and console their loved one, and each other, in his final hours.

After stroking Mr. John's face with cool washcloths, and tenderly touching his lips with wet mouth swabs and a generous slathering of Chapstick, they said their quiet good nights, with promises to return in the early morning. Each one gave Tom a kind pat on the head. He overheard Sharon giving the new night nurse instructions; then the voices faded away, and the ward fell silent. Tom made himself comfortable beside Mr. John's thigh, curled his tail over his nose, and went back to sleep. This time his dreams were filled with people and places from his past. Just as his mind was swimming up from sleep and towards the present time, he found himself in that netherworld between sleep and consciousness.

A voice came to him that he had heard before. "Tom, this is your destiny, your reason for being here at this very moment. At this place, in this time, you are the conductor on this train of life, and I am the final destination," said the voice. Tom, fully awake now, knew that the Lord had just spoken to him. Startled back into the present, he saw

Sharon sitting by her dad, gently rubbing his fingers, one by one.

Daylight was breaking, small slivers of light filtering through the blinds. Tom realized instantly that something in the room had changed. Mr. John's breathing was much shallower, so Tom moved closer to his parted lips and took a sniff. It confirmed what he already suspected; that his friend's journey in this life was near its end.

Crossing his paws in prayer, Tom spoke to his friend in his mind, letting him know that he wasn't alone. "Lord, please take Mr. John in a peaceful way, and may his journey to heaven be on the wings of angels," he prayed. He changed his position so that he was at the foot of the bed where he wouldn't interfere with his friend's daughter as she spoke to her dad.

"Dad, you have been the best father anyone could ever have. I know that you worry about Sabrina and the kids, but Charles and I will watch over them for you and keep them safe," she said, as she stood up. "Me, Tomcat, I'm exhausted, and I'm going outside to take a break, so please stay with my dad while I'm gone," she told Tom.

Maude came into the room as Sharon was leaving; they nodded to each other as they passed. Maude did all the usual checks on her patient; the very last procedure she did was to check his blood pressure.

Tom could tell by the look of concern on Maude's face that it was not good. She quickly left the room, calling for Ethel, who was at the nurses' station. Tom dared not move;

he knew the end was near, because the color in Mr. John's face had changed.

Outside, sitting alone on a bench, Sharon was remembering all the fun activities she and her dad had shared. She was lost in thought, but a rustling noise brought her back to the real world.

"What in the heck is that?" she thought to herself. She walked over to the flower bed, now just a mass of clumps of dead flowers and leaves, and she shifted the debris around to see what was making the noise. Lo and behold, laying there was the most beautiful cat, which had just given birth to the cutest and tiniest orange kitten.

"My word, this kitten is the spitting image of Tom—the same color, same markings," she said out loud. She bent down to the new mother: "Don't worry, mama cat, I'm not going to bother you and your new arrival," she said, as she replaced the flower clumps around them. "I had better get back to Dad's room; I've been gone way too long," she worriedly said under her breath.

Tom was keeping vigil as the doctors and nurses came in and out of Mr. John's room. He could tell by their hushed tones that his friend's suffering would be over soon. He heard Pastor Green, Doc Williams, and Mr. John's daughter speaking outside the partially opened door, and then he caught the sound of soft weeping. Tom moved closer to his friend's face and began his own version of a prayer to help him on his new journey.

He knew that Mr. John could still hear him pray.

Pastor Green and Sharon entered, the Pastor moving to the far side of the sickbed, Sharon sitting down in the old, brown easy chair on the side closer to the door. With all heads bowed, the pastor opened his bible and began his prayer for Mr. John's salvation and quick deliverance into heaven.

Tom had already told Mr. John that someone special would be waiting for him, and that he did not have to struggle anymore, because his soul had a beautiful place to go, and when Tom opened his eyes after the pastor said "amen," Mr. John had left this world, just as gentle as a lamb. He faintly heard his daughter telling him that she loved him as the pastor made his way over to her to put his hand on hers and give it a gentle pat. Maude, standing in the doorway, respectful of the seriousness of the moment, went directly to the worn pine dresser in the corner and pulled out the homemade American flag comforter donated to the Palliative Care Unit. She shooed Tom from the bed, and with much reverence and care, placed the quilt upon the body of a loyal American veteran. Then she left as quietly as she had come.

"Tom, you come here and lay with my dad for a while. You have made our burden lighter, and I know your presence here comforted Dad greatly," Sharon said, as she patted the spot at her father's feet. Tom took his place beside his friend and listened while his daughter spoke to her father in a soft whisper. They stayed that way for a bit, the cat watching for his friend's release and the daughter mourning her loss.

They both felt it at the same time: it was as if time stood still. Their gazes locked, cat and woman.

Then Tom looked up and away into the far corner of the room and marveled at the wondrous, miraculous sight. Mr. John's daughter knew what Tom was seeing. "I know you're there, Dad, because Tom has told on you— godspeed, Dad," she said lovingly. Tom saw his friend joyfully embraced by his sister Lucille, who had passed over only a week earlier. Mr. John looked into Tom's eyes, and from his spirit to Tom's, thanked him for his companionship—and with that, he was gone.

Tom looked down and away; he was utterly exhausted, but now that he really understood what his purpose was on this earth, he felt blessed. He left his friend's side when the family arrived; the grief they felt was too much for him to handle.

Echoes of Pastor Green's words about "a time to live and a time to die" still fresh in his mind, he remembered Miss Opal saying to him that when even the smallest of God's creatures dies, a new creation is born. "Life and death are mirror images," she'd told him.

Tom decided to go to his favorite window to look out over the grounds. He felt ashamed that thoughts of Sassy and his soon-to-be-family had slipped his mind. Festus, having never been at a loss for words before, was waiting for him at the window. The two of them sat in silence, each with his own thoughts.

Behind him, Tom heard Pastor Green and Doc coming down the hall. The pastor stopped to rub Tom's head. "It seems that it's going to be a beautiful day," he said.

"Yes sir, I would gladly agree with that statement," replied Doc.

"Absolutely, a great day, as a matter of fact. Mr. John's daughter just told me about a special event that occurred just before her dad passed away," smiled Pastor Green.

"I don't think I heard about it; what was it?" asked Doc.

"It seems that our Tomcat here has a secret, and if my old eyes aren't deceiving me, it's being revealed as we speak, said the pastor, pointing at something he could see from the window. "Look there at the fountain's edge," he said.

Tom stood up on his hind legs and pressed his face against the window pane, trying to make out what the pastor was referring to. Sitting near the fountain was the most gorgeous thing Tom had ever seen—Sassy, in all her glory, looking up toward the window that Tom was in. Their eyes met and you could feel the love between them.

Then Tom's gaze dropped to behold a miracle—the smallest of creatures, held by the nape of its neck, swaying back and forth like a rag doll, so orange it made your eyes hurt; and at Sassy's feet, a total replica of its mother, eyes closed, still wet from birth, tiny paws crossed in prayer-like fashion.

"I believe that congratulations are in order, Mr. Tom— you are a brand new dad!" everyone said at the same time. Tom's heart was so full of pride and joy at the sight of his new family that he lay down and crossed his paws to pray.

"Thank you, Lord, for my good fortune, and thank Mr. John, too," he prayed. "Now, don't that beat all, looks like he's praying or something," remarked Doc.

"Yep, that's exactly what he's doing, all right," agreed the pastor.

"I don't know if we can handle any more 'angel cats' in this-here establishment," said Doc, "but I guess we'll have to try," and they all laughed together.

The End

AUTHOR BIO

Sharon Kai Herndon lives and works in the Roanoke Valley surrounded by the beautiful Blue Ridge Mountains of Virginia. She enjoys writing, oil painting and rose gardening. Her book is about the spiritual journey her family undertook before the passing over of her father an Air Force veteran in December 2012 and the part a stray alley cat played in that solemn event. Tom continues to play a role in the lives of America's heroes our veterans who maybe at the end of their journeys in this world, Tom is the final salute to a job well done.

Made in the USA
Coppell, TX
02 March 2021

51077458R00076